The
BIG
Foreword by
Roger McGough

AMAZING
POETRY BOOK

The

Foreword by
Roger McGough

BIG

AMAZING

POETRY BOOK

52 WEEKS OF POETRY FROM 52 BRILLIANT POETS

CHOSEN BY GABY MORGAN AND ILLUSTRATED BY

Chris Riddell

MACMILLAN CHILDREN'S BOOKS

For Roger
Chris Riddell

For Chris Riddell – Champion of poets and poetry
Gaby x

Published 2022 by Macmillan Children's Books
an imprint of Pan Macmillan
The Smithson, 6 Briset Street, London EC1M 5NR
EU representative: Macmillan Publishers Ireland Ltd, 1st Floor,
The Liffey Trust Centre, 117–126 Sheriff Street Upper
Dublin 1, D01 YC43
Associated companies throughout the world
www.panmacmillan.com

ISBN 978-15290-9909-6

Collection compiled by Gaby Morgan

3 5 7 9 8 6 4 2

A CIP catalogue record for this book is available from the British Library.

Printed and bound by CPI Group (UK) Ltd, Croydon CR0 4YY

Contents

Liz Brownlee

Matt Goodfellow

Laura Mucha

Dom Conlon

Coral Rumble

James Carter

Valerie Bloom

John Rice

Kate Wakeling

Nick Toczek

Pie Corbett

Rachel Piercey

Kit Wright

Zaro Weil

Brian Patten

Julia Donaldson

Jenny Joseph

James Berry

Carol Ann Duffy

Gareth Owen

Grace Nichols

Peter Dixon

Clare Bevan

David Harmer

Eleanor Farjeon

Ian McMillan

Lewis Carroll

Steven Camden

Chrissie Gittins

Gerard Benson

Martin Glynn

A. F. Harrold

David Orme

Shauna Darling Robertson

John Foster

Mandy Coe

Ruth Awolola

John Agard

Wes Magee

Michaela Morgan

Foreword

The dictionary tells us that *a maze* is 'a complicated network of paths with walls or hedges designed as a challenge to find a way through.' Well, Gaby Morgan has indeed put together a book that will amaze, sometimes challenge, occasionally puzzle, but always delight young readers (up to, and including, 85 year olds). The Big Amazing Poetry Book is an *Annualogy*, in that it contains 7 poems (one for each day of the week) by 52 poets (one for each week of the year). Wow! You won't come across that very often. But unlike Time which is constantly on the move, you can set your own pace and dip in and out at your leisure.

What you have here is a galaxy of poems, each with a life of its own and a story to tell. You can open on any page and read, smile, sigh or snort and then move on. (*And nobody will notice if adventurous readers climb over walls or squeeze through hedges when nobody is looking!*) My hope is that after enjoying the journey, young readers will be encouraged to learn their favourites by heart, recite and better still, write their own verses, for writing can be an adventure, enabling us to move into a world of unlimited possibilities where we can be anybody, do anything. The writer, being in control of his or her own destiny, is given the opportunity to play the hero, score the goal, even settle old scores. Writing a poem can also be a way of telling others about our real lives, our fears and problems, a way of reaching out to somebody. And the key is one that we are all born with: Imagination. A key that can be mislaid, lost or simply taken away, often by an educational system whose emphasis is on facts and qualifications. All too often, imagination is replaced by *information* and day dreaming goes out of the window where it came from. It goes without saying, of course, that information is essential to human progress and survival, but then so is that ability to imagine another world, another future, another way of doing things.

Within these pages you will find poems by famous poets of the past like Lewis Carroll and Charles Causley as well those by famous poets of the future. This book is very much a celebration, not only of verse, but of the poets, most of whom I am proud to have met, who have spent much of their lives not only writing verse for children, but working their poetry socks off going into schools and spreading the good word. It is my sincere hope, and that of Gaby Morgan and all the poets featured here (as well as Chris Riddell whose drawings smile and wave at you from almost every page), that young readers will read all the poems, choose their favourites and share them with friends and family.

But finally, a word of warning: The danger of entering this maze of poetry is that you may enjoy yourself so much that you decide to stay where you are and never come out! Foreword is forewarned.

Roger McGough

Roger McGough

Born in Liverpool, Roger McGough wrote his first poem at the age of seventeen, became a teacher, sang on *Top of the Pops*, and received the Freedom of the City in 2001. Much travelled and translated, he has fathered four children and published more than a hundred books. A familiar voice on BBC Radio 4, he is President of the Poetry Society and in 2005 received a CBE from the Queen for his services to literature.

First Day at School

A millionbillionwillion miles from home
Waiting for the bell to go. (To go where?)
Why are they all so big, other children?
So noisy? So much at home they
must have been born in uniform.
Lived all their lives in playgrounds.
Spent the years inventing games
that don't let me in. Games
that are rough, that swallow you up.

And the railings.
All around, the railings.
Are they to keep out wolves and monsters?
Things that carry off and eat children?
Things you don't take sweets from?
Perhaps they're to stop us getting out.
Running away from the lessins. Lessin.
What does a lessin look like?
Sounds small and slimy.
They keep them in glassrooms.
Whole rooms made out of glass. Imagine.

I wish I could remember my name.
Mummy said it would come in useful.
Like wellies. When there's puddles.
Yellowwellies. I wish she was here.
I think my name is sewn on somewhere.
Perhaps the teacher will read it for me.
Tea-cher. The one who makes the tea.

Give and Take

I give you clean air. You give me poisonous gas
I give you mountains. You give me quarries

I give you pure snow. You give me acid rain
I give you spring fountains. You give me toxic canals

I give you a butterfly. You give me a plastic bottle
I give you a blackbird. You give me a cruise missile

I give you abundance. You give me waste
I give you one last chance. You give me excuse after excuse,

after excuse, after excuse......

The Sound Collector

A stranger called this morning
Dressed all in black and grey
Put every sound into a bag
And carried them away.

The whistling of the kettle
The turning of the lock
The purring of the kitten
The ticking of the clock

The popping of the toaster
The crunching of the flakes
When you spread the marmalade
The scraping noise it makes

The hissing of the frying-pan
The ticking of the grill
The bubbling of the bathtub
As it starts to fill

The drumming of the raindrops
On the window-pane
When you do the washing-up
The gurgle of the drain

The crying of the baby
The squeaking of the chair
The swishing of the curtain
The creaking of the stair

A stranger called this morning
He didn't leave his name
Left us only silence
Life will never be the same.

The Fight of the Year

'And there goes the bell for the third month
and Winter comes out of its corner looking groggy
Spring leads with a left to the head
followed by a sharp right to the body
    daffodils
    primroses
    crocuses
    snowdrops
    lilacs
    violets
    pussywillow
Winter can't take much more punishment
and Spring shows no signs of tiring
    tadpoles
    squirrels
    baalambs
    badgers
    bunny rabbits
    mad march hares
    horses and hounds

Spring is merciless
Winter won't go the full twelve rounds
    bobtail clouds
    scallywag winds
    the sun
    a pavement artist
    in every town
A left to the chin
and Winter's down!
    tomatoes
    radish
    cucumber
    onions
    beetroot
    celery
    and any
    amount
    of lettuce
    for dinner
Winter's out for the count
Spring is the winner!'

What I Love about School

What I love about school
    is the hurly-burly of the classroom,
    the sly humour of the teachers

What I hate about teachers
    is their reluctance to cartwheel
    down corridors

What I love about corridors
    is that the longer they are
    the louder the echo

What I hate about echo echo
    is its refusal to answer a straight
    question question

What I love about question
    is the proud admission
    of its own ignorance

What I hate about ignorance
    is the naive assumption
    that it is bliss

What I love about bliss
  is its willingness
  to rhyme with kiss

What I hate about kiss
  is the news of it going around
  like wildfire

What I love about wildfire
  is its dragon's breath
  and its hunger for life

What I hate about life
  is that as soon as you get the hang of it
  you run out of time

What I love about time
  is how it flies
  except when at school

What I hate about school
  is the hurly-burly of the playground,
  the sly humour of the teachers.

I'm Not as Nice as I Look

I may look nice on the cover
But once you open the book
You may be surprised to discover
I'm not as nice as I look

You could mistake me for a princess
With my long and flowing tresses
Eyes that shine like sapphires
And expensive hand-made dresses

I may look sweet and friendly
Full of charm and calm as can be
But inside I'm a raging inferno
A dark and stormy sea

My followers are my subjects
My kingdom is Instagram
A whirlwind of contradictions
A werewolf dressed as lamb

The one with my face on the cover
Please may I borrow that book?
But don't expect me to return it
I'm not as nice as I look.

Joy at the Sound

Joy at the silver birch fluffing its leaves
Joy at the bounce of the wagtail's tail

Joy at the swirl of cold milk in the blue bowl
Joy at the blink of its bubbles

Joy at the cat revving up on the lawn
Joy at the frogs that leapfrog to freedom

Joy at the screen that fizzes to life
Joy at The Simpsons, Lisa and Bart

Joy at the dentist: 'Fine, see you next year'
Joy at the school gates: 'Closed'

Joy at the sound of children at play
Joy at the bell at the end of the day

Joy at the silver withholding the chocolate
Joy at the poem, two verses to go

Joy at the zing of the strings of the racquet
Joy at the ping of the bright yellow ball

Joy at the key unlocking the door
Joy at the sound of your voice in the hall.

Brian Moses

Brian Moses was first published by Macmillan in 1996 and since then has had over fifty books published with the publishers, including his own poetry collections, poetry anthologies and picture books. His books have sold well over a million copies. *Lost Magic* is his 'Best Of' collection of his own poetry while his latest anthology is *The Best Ever Book of Funny Poems*. He has performed his poetry and percussion show at over 3,000 schools, libraries and festivals throughout the UK and abroad over the past thirty-four years. He was invited by Prince Charles to speak at the Prince's Summer School for teachers in 2007 and CBBC commissioned him to write a poem for the Queen on her 80th birthday. He lives in a village that was once home to Rudyard Kipling, with his wife, Anne, and their black labrador, Jess.

Days

Days fly by on holidays,
they escape like birds
released from cages.
What a shame you can't buy
tokens of time, save them up
and lengthen the good days,
or maybe you could tear out time
from days that drag, then pay it back
on holidays, wild days,
days you wish would last forever.
You could wear these days with pride,
fasten them like poppies to your coat,
or keep them in a tin, like sweets,
a confection of days
to be held on the tongue
and tasted, now and then.

Aliens Stole My Underpants

To understand the ways
of alien beings is hard,
and I've never worked it out
why they landed in my backyard.

And I've always wondered why
on their journey from the stars,
these aliens stole my underpants
and took them back to Mars.

They came on a Monday night
when the weekend wash had been done,
pegged out on the line
to be dried by the morning sun.

Mrs Driver from next door
was a witness at the scene
when aliens snatched my underpants –
I'm glad that they were clean!

It seems they were quite choosy
as nothing else was taken.
Do aliens wear underpants
or were they just mistaken?

I think I have a theory
as to what they wanted them for,
they needed to block off a draught
blowing in through the spacecraft door.

Or maybe some Mars museum
wanted items brought back from space.
Just think, my pair of Y-fronts
displayed in their own glass case.

And on the label beneath
would be written where they got 'em
and how such funny underwear
once covered an Earthling's bottom!

BRIAN'S
BOTTOM
COVER

Make Friends with a Tree

Give a tree a squeeze,
give a tree a hug,
join in celebration
with every bird and bug,

with every bat and badger,
with beetles and with bees,
a new year's resolution,
show kindness to the trees.

Make friends with a tree,
make friends with a tree,
hug a tree, go on show it
you really care, let a tree know it.
Make friends with a tree,
make friends with a tree.

Trees are always homes
to every sort of creature.
In a flat and empty landscape
a tree is a special feature.

Trees can be deciduous,
pine trees are coniferous,
but trees will never hurt you
no tree is carnivorous!

16

So treat a tree politely,
show it you're sincere.
Long after we have disappeared
trees will still be here.

Make friends with a tree,
make friends with a tree,
hug a tree, go on show it
you really care, let a tree know it.
Make friends with a tree,
make friends with a tree.

Snuggle up to a sycamore,
cuddle up to a pine,
wrap your arms around an oak,
enjoy a joke with a lime.

A tree will always listen,
tell your troubles to a tree.
To the mystery of life
an ash may hold the key.

So don't be abrupt with a birch,
don't try to needle a pine.
Don't interrupt a horse chestnut,
don't give a tree a hard time.

Make friends with a tree,
make friends with a tree,
hug a tree, go on show it
you really care, let a tree know it.
Make friends with a tree,
make friends with a tree.

A tree is a living thing,
it's not just a lump of wood.
Trees in Sherwood Forest
know all about Robin Hood.

A tree can tell us stories,
a tree knows history,
so in this world of fake and sham
let's celebrate truth in a tree.

Make friends with a tree,
make friends with a tree,
hug a tree, go on show it
you really care, let a tree know it.
Make friends with a tree,
make friends with a tree.

Lost Magic

Today I found some lost magic –
a twisty-twirly horn
of a unicorn lying at my feet.
And when I stopped
to pick it up, to hold it
in my fist, I remembered
how once upon a time
you could always find unicorns,
but there are no unicorns now.

You would find them on the shoreline,
flitting in and out of caves in cliffs,
or climbing hills at twilight.
They would lead you through forests,
sometimes hiding behind trees,
and if you lost them or they lost you,
you could always find them again,
but there are no unicorns now.

And it didn't matter
if you followed them all day,
the edge of the world was miles away,
there was nothing to fear.
And none of the unicorns we knew ever
changed into dangerous strangers.

Once upon a time there *were* unicorns
but there are no unicorns now.

A Feather from an Angel

Anton's box of treasures held
a silver key and a glassy stone,
a figurine made of polished bone
and a feather from an angel.

The figurine was from Borneo,
the stone from France or Italy,
the silver key was a mystery
but the feather came from an angel.

We might have believed him if he'd said
the feather fell from a bleached white crow
but he always replied, 'It's an angel's, I know,
a feather from an angel.'

We might have believed him if he'd said,
'An albatross let the feather fall.'
But he had no doubt, no doubt at all,
his feather came from an angel.

'I thought I'd dreamt him one night,' he'd say,
'but in the morning I knew he'd been there;
he left a feather on my bedside chair,
a feather from an angel.'

And it seems that all my life I've looked
for the sort of belief that nothing could shift,
something simple and precious as Anton's gift,
a feather from an angel.

Walking with my Iguana

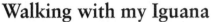

*Words in brackets to be replaced by
another voice or voices*

I'm walking (I'm walking)
with my iguana (with my iguana)

I'm walking (I'm walking)
with my iguana (with my iguana)

When the temperature rises
to above eighty-five,
my iguana is looking
like he's coming alive.

So we make it to the beach,
my iguana and me,
then he sits on my shoulder
as we stroll by the sea . . .

and I'm walking (I'm walking)
with my iguana (with my iguana)

I'm walking (I'm walking)
with my iguana (with my iguana)

21

Well if anyone sees us
we're a big surprise,
my iguana and me
on our daily exercise,

till somebody phones
the local police
and says I have an alligator
tied to a leash

when I'm walking (I'm walking)
with my iguana (with my iguana)

I'm walking (I'm walking)
with my iguana (with my iguana)

It's the spines on his back
that make him look grim,
but he just loves to be tickled
under his chin.

And my iguana will tell me
that he's ready for bed
when he puts on his pyjamas
and lays down his sleepy (Yawn) head.

And I'm walking (I'm walking)
with my iguana (with my iguana)

still walking (still walking)
with my iguana (with my iguana)

with my iguana . . .

with my iguana . . .

and my piranha

and my chihuahua

and my chinchilla,

with my groovy gorilla

my caterpillar . . .

and I'm walking . . .

with my iguana . . . . . .

All the Things You Can Say to Places in the UK

Always say 'Ta' to Leamington Spa,
say 'Have a nice day' to Whitley Bay.
You can shout 'What's new?' or even 'Howdo'
to inhabitants of Looe or Crewe.
You can tell the whole story in Tobermory,
say 'Hi' to Rye and 'Right on' to Brighton,
or call out 'Let's go' to Plymouth Hoe.
Talk through your dreams in Milton Keynes,
say 'It's all for the best' in Haverfordwest.
Always say 'Yes' when you visit Skegness
but only say 'No' in Llandudno.
Don't tell a lie to the Island of Skye
or say 'It smells' in Tunbridge Wells.
Don't talk rude if you're down in Bude
or start to get gabby in Waltham Abbey.
Don't ever plead in Berwick on Tweed
or say 'You look ill' to Burgess Hill.
You could lose your voice and talk with your hands
when you take a trip to Camber Sands,
but whatever you say just won't impress
the inhabitants of Shoeburyness.

Sue Hardy-Dawson

Sue Hardy-Dawson is a poet and illustrator and lives in North Yorkshire with her husband, Mark, and two bouncy spaniels. It is not unusual to find her loudly reciting poetry to dogs and trees whilst walking about in the countryside. Sue started writing poems for her own children and now she has lots of poems in anthologies as well as two solo collections, *Where Zebras Go* and *If I Were Other Than Myself*. *Apes to Zebras* written with her two friends, Roger Stevens and Liz Brownlee, won the North Somerset Teachers' Book Awards in 2018.

When she was young she hated writing because she couldn't spell many worms very well as she has something called Dyslexia. Because of this, Sue loves visiting schools and helping children write poetry, especially those who don't think they like to read and write.

Mother Tongue

Cloud is not my first language
I understand a few words
their greeting for morning
three silent names for a storm
those for light and air
eight words for sky
I have tried to write
but how to spell them

I cannot speak stone, ancient
igneous, always changed
its rune-words half fossil
guttural and glacial
all rough consonants
five words for cracks
eight for avalanche
and as for mountain . . .

Naturally I'm fluent
in tree, ponderous creatures
ah but they don't say much
when they do it's a whisper
one word for root
for everything
it's just percussion
without the diction

26

And who ever knew water
mostly it just babbles, fish
speak some and pebbles
you think you understand
then it bursts banks
or just dries up
and then when it rains
no punctuation

27

Dazzle Dance

I am made of heat and light
comets spinning through the night
spit and splinter – meteorite
firecracker, pinwheel bright.

I am made from ash and coal
watch my embers wax and glow
twist and turn my body so
dragon breath to volcano.

I have frazzle crackle hands
dance a razzle dazzle dance
simmer swirling twist and prance
glitter, sparkle to entrance.

I am made of cinder stars
gasses burning from afar
supernova in the dark
flash of thunder full of spark.

I incinerate and blaze
candles burning in my gaze
born of fire, heat and flame
come and bask beneath my rays.

Snail Spell

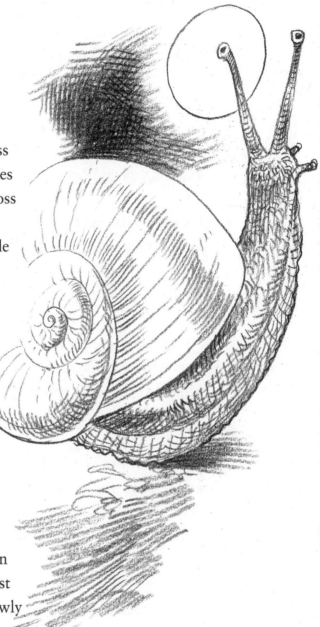

Snail you
prosper slippery
in rain's looking glass
dropping crystal runes
on velvet folds of moss

skimming four pebble
toad bronze eyes
across leaf lakes
of autumn fire

till dusk

then you pick
at the moon
scraps of sky
taste the earth gold
on breath of night

over flower mountain
dank, strawberry mist
you eat darkness slowly
until it leaves.

Learning by Heart

A poem is not just
the sum of its parts.
The number of lines
where its metaphors are.

It's not about digging
for meaning in stanzas.
It's a secret between us.
There are no wrong answers.

It's not some sort of test
a code to be cracked.
More a spell for a dreamer
or a musical map.

It just wants to be loved
not to fill you with dread.
Let it flow like a river
through the space in your head.

Let it sing you to sleep
hear its echoes in stars.
Find one piece you can keep
learn the rest with your heart . . .

Rhythms

I'm the rhythm of lilting leaves
The syllables of sleeping trees
The rude rhymes of roots beneath
The song of soil's earth-heartbeat

I'm the rhythm of shifting sky
The subtle strains of warm sunlight
The whistle of a wind's sharp sigh
The ripple of rain's moonless night

I'm the rhythm of salt and spray
The patter of pebbles over shale
The weft of weed on watery grave
The wet percussion of the waves

I am the rhythm of dial and clock
The ageless face that time mocks
The hour's chimes, ticks and tocks
The sounds of life until it stops

The Creak

In
the
attic
lives a
Creak. Does
anyone know
what Creaks eat?
Sometimes he hides,
Up the stairs,
With Squeak and Growl,
who both live there.
Their friend Tip Tap's,
A proper pain,
jabbing at the
window frame.
On windy nights
Whoosh comes in too,
he likes the vent,
behind the loo.
No one likes,
Whoosh in the attic,
Creak and Squeak,
make such a racket,
Tip Tap bangs,
to be let in,
but Growl
creates
the biggest din.
Soon old Whoosh is sulking hard,
kicking bins around the yard,
tearing leaves off, clanking gates,
screeching and howling in pipes and grates,
In the attic lives a Creak,
and on the stairs,
live Growl and Squeak,
Tip Tap and Whoosh,
Fought all this week,
and I just want a bit of peace.

The Tinsel Tree

I
did
not grow
on mountain
slopes, fragrant
with pine, bitter wind.
I am the dull silver of ages,
worn thin with ancient baubles,
paper stars, candy-stripe-lanterns.
My twigs curled tight in their nesting
box, creak out each year, when cold light
enters. Rusted limbs, unfurled, to drop wire
bones. My scent is the waxing moths and dusty
shimmers, their spun silk, gaudy filaments of glass.
Here are my winter blooms; dry plaster, stamen-candles,
glinting with crepe flames. Still, I hold close, three decades of
laughter.
My treasures made precious by
tiny hands – give the miracles
of stucco angels. To dance light
on gilt fir cones, scarlet beads.
All, glow softly, breathing
midnight carols.

Joseph Coelho

Joseph Coelho is the current Children's Laureate. He grew up in the last village in London, in Roehampton during the 1980's and lived in a tower block with his mum and little sister. He studied archaeology at university (the study of the physical past) and dug up bones in Peru for a couple of years which was lots of fun but he also wrote poems and started directing and writing plays. His first poetry collection *Werewolf House Rules* was published in 2014 and he has been writing and performing ever since.

Make It Bigger, Eileen!

In Art I drew a park
with a pond, and railings, and children playing . . .
and trees with multi-coloured leaves
and mothers with pushchairs wearing hats that jumped
and joggers running with three legs
and skaters – skating on thin ice with elephants on their backs
and pigeons playing cards on bread tables
and grass with eyes and noses
and flowers with walking sticks and headphones
and clouds that rained smells
and a sun as deep as an ocean
and stones that bled
and a rainbow with stairs.

Sir said . . .

'Tut, tut, tut. Bigger, Eileen,
your picture must be bigger.'

So I drew a duck.

Miss Flotsam

Miss Flotsam was my reception teacher.
She had travelled the world.
Brown hair turned golden
under distant suns,
clothes carrying colours
from countless corners of continents.

When my mother's face spilled
a gush of adolescent tears
at the school gates,
Miss Flotsam soaked up the drops
in Peruvian alpaca,
caught splashes
in Himalayan singing bowls,
let sobs fall on Indonesian Gamelans.

Miss Flotsam had flown
through air pockets in jumbo jets,
sailed the seven seas
in opposite directions,
cycled through cyclones
with dengue fever,
soothed mothers
when their hearts heaved.

When the bully punched me
for being too brown,
Miss Flotsam glared at him
with an eye that could turn fists
into begging bowls.

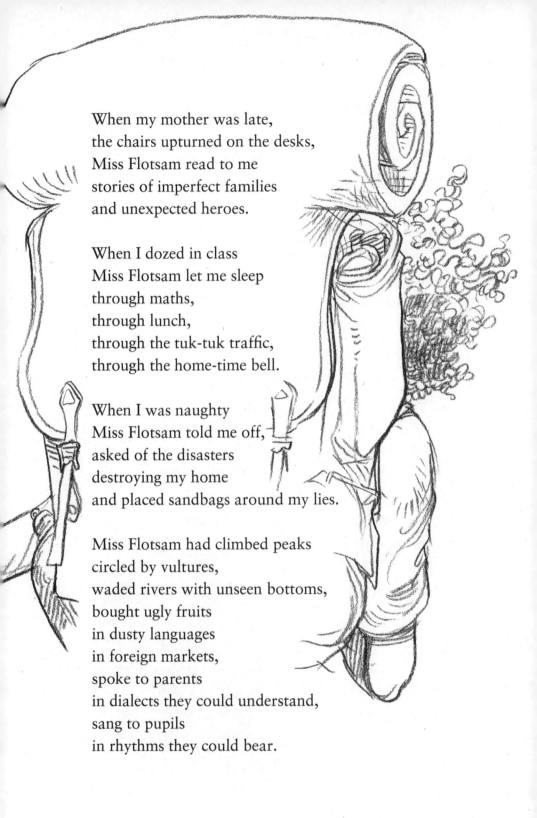

When my mother was late,
the chairs upturned on the desks,
Miss Flotsam read to me
stories of imperfect families
and unexpected heroes.

When I dozed in class
Miss Flotsam let me sleep
through maths,
through lunch,
through the tuk-tuk traffic,
through the home-time bell.

When I was naughty
Miss Flotsam told me off,
asked of the disasters
destroying my home
and placed sandbags around my lies.

Miss Flotsam had climbed peaks
circled by vultures,
waded rivers with unseen bottoms,
bought ugly fruits
in dusty languages
in foreign markets,
spoke to parents
in dialects they could understand,
sang to pupils
in rhythms they could bear.

Hamster! Hamster!

We've got a hamster in our class,
as brown as toffee.
He's so sweet, so cute,
with chubby cheeks
for storing nuts and fruit.
He sips from a water bottle
strapped to his cage,
like a little baby!
Awww, he's soooooo cute.
He's got these darling little paws
like a doll's hands,
and a sweet, cute, tiny little tail
like a little piece of spaghetti!
Awwwww, he is soooooo deliciously cute.

One day I put my finger up to his cage,
and he sniffed it with a nose
like a chocolate-chip button
and he . . . BIT ME!

We've got a hamster in our class,
as brown as a bog.
He is so mean, so horrible,
with fat cheeks
for storing pupils' fingers.
He sucks at a water bottle
strapped to his cage,
like a greedy rat!
Errr, he's soooooo disgusting.
He's got these vicious claws
as terrible as a tiger's,
and a long, wiggerly, squiggerly tail
as scaly as a snake!

ARRRRR

he is soooooo perfectly horrid!

Siblings

Like the Three Musketeers
we were all for one.

Like the Three Blind Mice
we saw without looking.

Like the Three Bowls of Porridge
we were just right.

Like the Three Sisters
we were sad inside.

Like the Three Billy Goats Gruff
we feared the troll.

Like the Three Little Pigs
we longed for our own home.

Like the Three Wishes
we were never enough.

Conquer

Five children clasping mittens
could not hug the entire trunk.
Whole hands could hide in the folds of its bark.
James, the tallest boy in class,
could sit on a root,
his feet would not touch the ground.

Every classroom faced the playground,
every child could see the tree.
Leaves beckoning.
Conkers swelling.

As the bells rang
we'd march to the tree,
sticks in hand,
eyes fixed on the mace-like horse chestnuts.
Green spikes hungry to prick
our minds obsessed by the jewels within.

If all the world were paper

If all the world were paper
I would fold up my gran
and take her everywhere I go.
I would laminate my baby sister in bubble wrap
and lay her to sleep in unbound fairy-tale book pages.
And should she get scared,
rip every fear,
shred every scream,
tear every tear.

If all the world were paper
I would re-bind my grandfather,
smooth out the dog-ears to all his stories,
place his younger days in a zoetrope
and flush the harrowing chapters
down an ink-gurgling well.

If all the world were paper
kind deeds would be post-it notes
that stick to the doer in ever-growing trails,
so we would always remember,
friends would come with perforated lines
so you could keep their best bits with you
at all times.

If all the world were paper
Christmas wrapping foil and birthday cards
would follow you to school.

If all the world were paper
dreams would be Braille
so we could read them whilst we slept,
nightmares would be shopping lists
because shopping lists are so easy to forget.

If all the world were paper
arguments would rustle before they started
and could be put right with a little tape.

If all the world were paper
we could paperclip families together,
draw smiles on all the sad faces,
rub out the tears,
cover our homes in Tippex and start all over again.

All the world is not paper,
but whilst we can imagine it were
we can recycle the rough times
knowing we will never fold.

Books Have Helped Me

Books have more images between their words
than any smart phone could hold.
More flavours than a thousand jelly beans.
More lives for you to live
than any computer game.

Books have helped me.

I've read about characters
who have laughed, cried and sighed like me.

Characters who have battled
monsters larger than any I could imagine.

Characters who have travelled distances longer
than there are miles between me and the sun.

When I thumb through a book
their pages whisper to me
that I'll be all right.

Paul Cookson

10 things you might not know about Paul

1. He was born in 1961, adopted and brought up in Lancashire.
2. He published his first booklet when he was eighteen.
3. Since then, he has published over sixty collections and sold over a million books.
4. He has visited thousands of schools, making children and teachers laugh and love poetry for over thirty years.
5. He is Poet in Residence at the National Football Museum.
6. He was commissioned by Everton FC to write a poem for their season ticket campaign (Home), which was made into a film.
7. He has a football team of ukuleles, four of them electric.
8. During Lockdown he started writing and sharing a new poem every day on social media.
9. Not only is he Poet Laureate for Slade, he is in a band with their original drummer – Don Powell.
10. He is lyric Writer in Residence for Let's Go Sing.
11. Maths was never his strong point.

Let No One Steal Your Dreams

Let no one steal your dreams
Let no one tear apart
The burning of ambition
That fires the drive inside your heart.

Let no one steal your dreams
Let no one tell you that you can't
Let no one hold you back
Let no one tell you that you won't.

Set your sights and keep them fixed
Set your sights on high
Let no one steal your dreams
Your only limit is the sky.

Let no one steal your dreams
Follow your heart
Follow your soul
For only when you follow them
Will you feel truly whole.

Set your sights and keep them fixed
Set your sights on high
Let no one steal your dreams
Your only limit is the sky.

Coolscorin' Matchwinnin' Celebratin' Striker!

I'm a shirt removin' crowd salutin'
handstandin' happy landin'
rockin' rollin' divin' slidin'
posin' poutin' loud shoutin'
pistol packin' smoke blowin'
flag wavin' kiss throwin'
hipswingin' armwavin'
breakdancin' cool ravin'
shoulder shruggin' team huggin'
hot shootin' rootin' tootin'
somersaultin' fence vaultin'
last-minute goal grinnin'
shimmy shootin' shin spinnin'
celebratin' cup winnin' STRIKER!

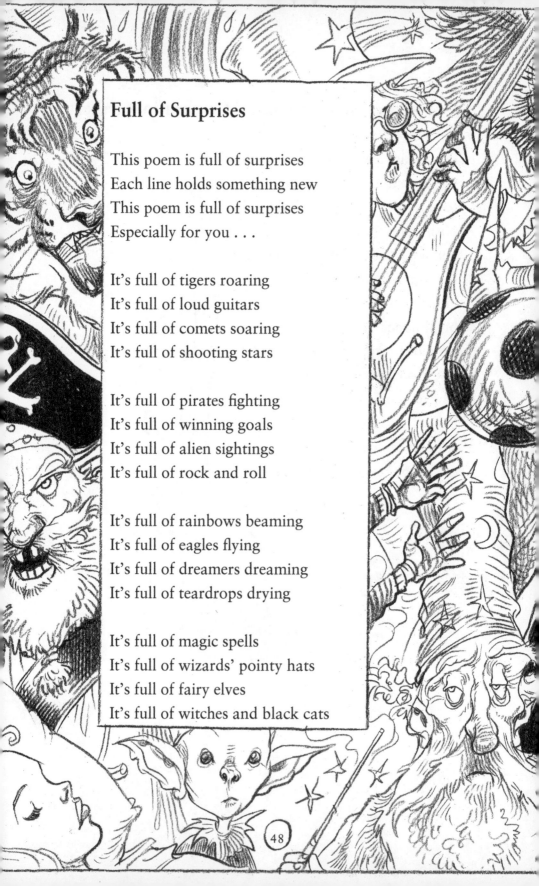

Full of Surprises

This poem is full of surprises
Each line holds something new
This poem is full of surprises
Especially for you . . .

It's full of tigers roaring
It's full of loud guitars
It's full of comets soaring
It's full of shooting stars

It's full of pirates fighting
It's full of winning goals
It's full of alien sightings
It's full of rock and roll

It's full of rainbows beaming
It's full of eagles flying
It's full of dreamers dreaming
It's full of teardrops drying

It's full of magic spells
It's full of wizards' pointy hats
It's full of fairy elves
It's full of witches and black cats

It's full of dragons breathing fire
It's full of dinosaurs
It's full of mountains reaching higher
It's full of warm applause

It's full of everything you need
It's full of more besides
It's full of food, the world to feed
It's full of fairground rides

It's full of love and happiness
It's full of dreams come true
It's full of things that are the best
Especially for you

It's jammed and crammed and packed and stacked
With things both old and new
This poem is full of surprises
Especially for you.

Crazy at the Zoo

There's a penguin eating pizza
A lion in the loo
A bear that wears pink underwear
It's crazy at the zoo

A rock and rolling rhino
A kung fu kangaroo
A hip hop hippopotamus
It's crazy at the zoo

A ballet dancing buffalo
In a tiny tutu too
An elephant in spotty pants
It's crazy at the zoo

The zebra's stripes are painted
Orange, red and blue
The tiger's pink and purple
It's crazy at the zoo

A gecko with an echo
Is g-nagging the gnu
A giggling gorilla
It's crazy at the zoo

A parrot that is potty
Sings Cock a doodle doo
A crocodile with a toothless smile
It's crazy at the zoo

Monkeys wearing lipstick
Bonkers but it's true
Snakes in socks are tied in knots
It's crazy at the zoo

An orangutan that tangoes
With a cockatoo
A sloth that coughs and races off
It's crazy at the zoo

All the clever keepers
Know just what to do
They're selling lots of tickets
Lots and lots of tickets

Selling lots more tickets
Because . . .
It's crazy – at – the zoo !

Go Explore the Countryside

A summer's day, a bunch of friends
Bows and arrows, building dens
Make believe and let's pretend
All of this and much more when
Finding tallest trees to climb
Leave reality behind
Hide and seek and lots to find
Losing track of space and time
A place to chase and seek and hide
Go explore the countryside

Rope swings over muddy ditches
Stepping stones and building bridges
Snagging clothes on hawthorn hedges
Balancing on stony ledges
Buttercups beneath the chin
Spinning jennies spin and spin
Grass between the thumbs that sing
Dock leaf cures for nettle stings
Hikes to hike and bikes to ride
Go explore the countryside

A piece of penknife poetry
Initialled love hearts there to see
Carved graffiti on the tree
From here to eternity
Flat and smooth skimming stones

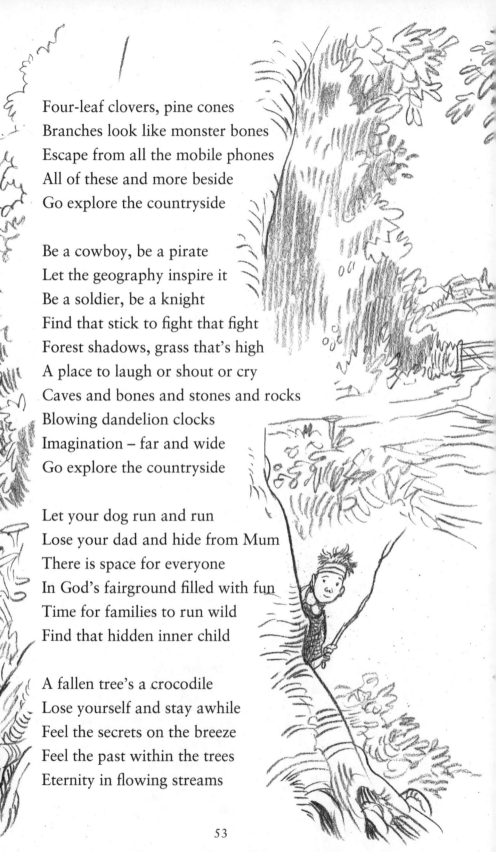

Four-leaf clovers, pine cones
Branches look like monster bones
Escape from all the mobile phones
All of these and more beside
Go explore the countryside

Be a cowboy, be a pirate
Let the geography inspire it
Be a soldier, be a knight
Find that stick to fight that fight
Forest shadows, grass that's high
A place to laugh or shout or cry
Caves and bones and stones and rocks
Blowing dandelion clocks
Imagination – far and wide
Go explore the countryside

Let your dog run and run
Lose your dad and hide from Mum
There is space for everyone
In God's fairground filled with fun
Time for families to run wild
Find that hidden inner child

A fallen tree's a crocodile
Lose yourself and stay awhile
Feel the secrets on the breeze
Feel the past within the trees
Eternity in flowing streams

53

Rugged rocks and crystal seams
In this eternal field of dreams

Go explore, go explore
Go explore – it's what it's for
All of this and much, much more
Mother Nature's superstore
Where geography, biology
And history all collide
There's majesty and mystery
Passing time for me and you
Lots of things to make and do
Yesterdays or something new
Go explore – you know it's true

The magic here, the magic there
Take your time to stop and stare
Be sanctified and goggle-eyed
Satisfied and gratified
Come back to
Come back to
The magic of the countryside

Friends for Ever

If you laugh
I'll laugh too

If you cry
I'll cry with you

If you're sad
I'll hold your hand

I will try
To understand

I will listen
If you talk

I will follow
When you walk

If you dance
We'll dance together

We can be
Friends for ever

Sea Shoals See Shows on the Sea Bed

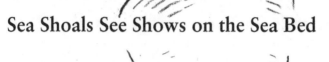

The salmon with a hat on
Was conducting with a baton
And it tried to tune a tuna fish
By playing on its scales
But the scales had all been flattened
When the tuna fish was sat on
On purpose by a porpoise
And a school of killer whales

So the salmon with a hat on
Fiddled with a baton
The angelfish got ready
To play the tambourine
Things began to happen
When the salmon with a baton
Was tapping out a pattern
For the band of the marines

There was a minnow on piano
A prawn with a horn
An otter on guitar
Looking all forlorn
A whale voice choir
A carp with a harp
A belly-dancing jellyfish
Jiving with a shark

The octaves on the octopus
Played the middle eight
But they couldn't keep in time
With the skiffle-playing skate
The plaice on the bass
Began to rock and roll
With a bloater in a boater
And a Dover sole

A clam on castanets
An eel on glockenspiel
An oyster in a cloister
Singing with a seal
The haddock had a headache
From the deafening din
And the sword-dancing sword fish
Sliced off a fin

A limpet on a trumpet, a flatfish on a flute
The kipper fell asleep with King Canute
Barracuda on a tuba sat upon a rock
The electric eel gave everyone a shock

The shrimp and the sturgeon
The stingray and the squid
Sang a four-part harmony
On the sea bed
The crab and the lobster
Gave their claws a flick

Kept everyone in time
With a click click click

Kept everyone in time with a click click click . . .
Kept everyone in time with a click click click . . .

Yes the salmon with a hat on
Was tapping out a pattern
And things began to happen
For the band of the marines
It was an ocean of commotion of Atlantic proportion
The greatest show by schools of shoals
That ever had been seen

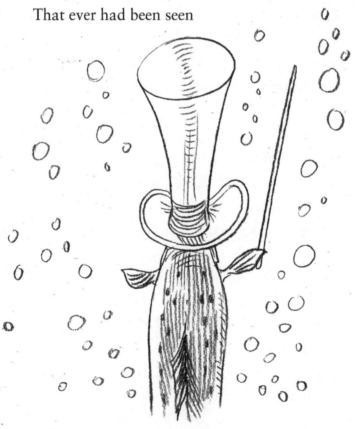

58

Nikita Gill

Nikita Gill is a British-Indian poet, playwright, writer and illustrator living in the south of England. She has published five collections of poetry: *Your Soul Is A River*, *Your Heart is the Sea*, *Wild Embers*, *Fierce Fairytales* and *Great Goddesses*. She is the editor of the poetry anthology *SLAM!* and her new collection is *These Are the Words*.

The Cat on Autumn Days

The first chill brings the cat in sooner,
and the cat always knows when you are sad.
So she tries in her cat way to make you feel better,
brings a mouse home that manages to escape,
causes chaos while your mum is trying to bake,
but also laughter where you once held sadness.

Later, she'll fall asleep on your lap,
Long black tail curled around your arm protectively,
A tiny purring warm shape that melts away your worries.
There are people who say cats don't know how to love.
What they do not know is cats do love,
they just love differently.

Hanging Out

I don't think I've ever been happier
Than when hanging out with you
And you tell me the silliest story about your day.

Tell it again
So we can become cascades of laughter
For the third time today.

On the First Flowers of Spring

The thrush is building a nest
right outside your bedroom window,

and the freshly thawed breeze
brings hope into your now green garden.

The flowers you planted last year
sing in yellow and pink blooms,

spring and you are soulmates,
life blossoming everywhere for you,

filled with healing and promise.

Reminder on Friendship

Some friends are temporary,
Not because you hurt them
Or they hurt you.

But because friendships
Are like seasons sometimes.

Outgrowing a friend may hurt
But it's something you must do.

Every meadow
must let go of its flowers in winter,
so it can grow fresh ones in spring.

A Short List of Alternatives

Climb a tree
Or drink some tea
Or spend some time
with your family

Write a song
Or sing along
To your favourite popstars'
Newest songs

Make memes and laugh away
Or watch films or write a play
Or leave your pajamas on and stay
Indoors reading all day today.

Go for a walk
Or have a heartfelt talk
Or paint a rock
Or knit some socks.

I could go on
But I'm running out of room
Yet I think you get
What I'm trying to say

There's a thousand
Better things to do today
Instead of being mean or sending hate
Someone else's way.

On the First Wave of Summer

Too old for scraped knees and playgrounds
And running after ice cream trucks.

But still young enough to sit on the docks,
Feet just touching the ice-cold water,

Strawberries, ice lollies and sticky fingers.
This is a litany of crushes and hopeful probabilities,

Welcome to almost womanhood
And a summer of possibilities.

93 Per Cent Stardust

After Carl Sagan, who gave me hope as a child

We have calcium in our bones,
iron in our veins,
carbon in our souls
and nitrogen in our brains.

93 per cent stardust,
with souls made of flames,
we are all just stars
that have people names.

Jan Dean

Jan Dean is from the North West of England, but now lives in the South West, having slipped down the map all the way to Devon (where she likes to swim in the cold sea). She has written hundreds of poems most of which have been published by Macmillan. She has visited schools all over Britain and performed poems and run workshops in Europe and New Zealand. She has a tall husband and two even taller sons and a tall daughter-in-law. They all put things on shelves she can't reach. But when she is having fun making up juicy words they all join in.

It's Not What I'm Used to

I don't want to go to Juniors . . .

The chairs are too big
I like my chair small, so I fit
Exactly
And my knees go
Just so
Under the table.

And that's another thing –
The tables are too big.
I like my table to be
Right
For me
So my workbook opens
Properly.
And my pencil lies in the space at the top
The way my thin cat stretches into a long line
On the hearth at home.

Pencils – there's another thing.
Another problem.
Up in Juniors they use pens and ink.
I shall really have to think

About ink.

Angels

We are made from light.
Called into being we burn
Brighter than the silver white
of hot magnesium.
More sudden than yellow phosphorus.
We are the fire of heaven;
Blue flames and golden ether.

We are from stars.
Spinning beyond the farthest galaxy
In an instant gathered to this point
We shine, speak our messages and go,
Back to brilliance.
We are not separate, not individual,
We are what we are made of. Only
Shaped sometimes into tall-winged warriors,
Our faces solemn as swords,
Our voices joy.

The skies are cold;
Suns do not warm us;
Fire does not burn itself.
Only once we touched you
And felt a human heat.
Once, in the brightness of the frost.
Above the hills, in glittering starlight,
Once, we sang.

Midnight

Sleep is another country
We visit in our head.
I watch my brother sleeping now –
His eyelids heavy-smooth as lead . . .
A million miles away from me
Across our bedroom, in his bed.

It feels as if there's only me,
I'm the last boy left alive,
After the end of everything –
The last one to survive . . .
The screech owl cries, the wild wolf howls
The whole wide world's an ache.

For I am the last and lonely one
The only one left awake.

Tent

In my tent
The light is orange.
And I sit here
Still
As if I'm set in jelly.

It's magic here
In this gold space
Where a minute stretches on . . .
    and on . . . and on . . .

Rosa Parks

In 1955 Rosa Parks refused to move from her seat in the 'whites only' part of the bus. This was an important event in the American Civil Rights movement – fighting for equal treatment for black people.

she sorts the drawer
knives at the left
forks at the right
spoons in the middle
like neat silver petals
curved inside each other

the queue sorts itself
snaking through the bus
whites at the front
blacks at the back

but people are not knives
not forks
not spoons
their bones are full of stardust
their hearts full of songs
and the sorting on the bus
is just plain wrong

so Rosa says no
and Rosa won't go
to the place for her race

she'll face up to all the fuss
but she's said goodbye
to the back of the bus

June 1963

*Valentina Tereshkova was the first woman to fly in
space. (She'd told her mother she was going on a
parachute course when in fact she was going to orbit
the Earth.) The most famous photograph of her shows
her smiling.*

Valentina smiles
    From Vostok 6 the world looks fragile
    somewhere down there the Volga flows
    her father drives his tractor
    and her mother's working in the cotton mill.

Valentina smiles
    Fills in her logbook
    checks the instruments
    watches the lovely Earth
    as she revolves in steady orbit.

Valentina smiles
    ALONE for three days
    circling and circling our planet.
    The sky is black and full of stars . . .

Valentina smiles
    We watch her on TV,
    millions of us see that smile
    and wonder what she's thinking.

Valentina smiles
    She dreams of parachutes
    round as the domes of jellyfish
    of diving through the sky
    borne up by curved white silk.
    She falls in love with space
and smiles.

Colouring in

And staying inside the lines
Is fine, but . . .
I like it when stuff leaks –
When the blue bird and the blue sky
Are just one blur of blue blue flying,
And the feeling of the feathers in the air
And the wind along the blade of wing
Is a long gash of smudgy colour.
I like it when the flowers and the sunshine
Puddle red and yellow into orange,
The way the hot sun on my back
Lulls me – muddles me – sleepy
In the scented garden,
Makes me part of the picture . . .
Part of the place.

Roger Stevens

Roger Stevens has been making poetry fun for a long time. He has over forty books for children to his name and is loved as much for his serious poems as for those that make us laugh. His award-winning website, The Poetry Zone, has been publishing poems by children for twenty-five years and gives great ideas to teachers and parents on how to share and enjoy poetry. He has performed his work on radio, at big events and in schools, where he also runs workshops. He is a National Poetry Day Ambassador. Roger, his wife and their very shy dog Jasper divide their time between their house in France and their flat in Brighton.

Mum & Dad

Tenderskin & Roughchin
Dawngreeter & Toastjuggler
Cuddlebear & Grizzlybear
Firmhand & Strongarm
Sadsmile & Grinner
Busybee & Grasshopper
Spicegrinder & Potstirrer
Sunsoaker & Ballspinner
Spidershrieker & Jarcatcher
Taleteller & Dreamweaver
Earthmother & Earthmover

A Dog's Conundrum

It might seem obvious to you humans
But it puzzles me every day
If he wants the stick so badly

Why does he throw it away?

The Estuary Field Trip

I walked with my class along the estuary
The salty wind sneaked through the cracked concrete
of time-worn sea defences,
stirred the weeds and rusty wire
that rose from the caked mud bed.
Thirty children poked under rocks
hunting for crabs
and tugged at a lump of driftwood,
perhaps once part of a sailing barge
taking bricks to London.

Isn't it beautiful? I said
Richard looking at me, nodded, smiled
A rare moment
A mystical union of teacher and pupil
Mr Stevens, said Richard,
Did you see the Man U game last night?

Corrections

Teacher said,
Leave out the the,
two too's one too too many
and and after the comma
should go after the any.

The the, the too –
and move the and
and that should make it flow.
Not that that, that that's fine –
but this that, that could go.

I said,
The the, the too, the and –
I would agree with you.
But I am very fond of that –
this that and that that too.

Which that is that?
Is that this that?
Asked teacher with a grin.
OK – but take that last in out
And leave that last out in.

Longing for Wide Open Spaces

Do
You ever
Feel that the
World is closing in?
Asif thereis notime tothink
Asyouwalk alongthestreet
Peoplejostlingandpushing
And you want to shout
Givemesomeroomtobreathe
Andyoudreamofclamberinghighhills
Climbingabovethecrowdsinthewideopencountryside
Just y o u

A l o n e   w i t h   t h e

F   o   r   e   v   e   r

s   k   y

Chalk

As we walk across this hill of chalk
It's hard to imagine
That once these hills
Were below the sea
Chalk is the sediment
Left by a million tiny creatures
On the seabed
I think of that
As we walk upon this thin skin
Of earth and grass
Beneath the blue sky
And a burning sun

Hallowe'en

Darren's got a pumpkin
Hollowed out a treat
He put it in the window
It scared half the street

I wish I had a pumpkin
But I've not and it's a shame
I've got a scary carrot
But it's not the same

Charles Causley

Charles Causley was one of England's most distinguished poets. Ted Hughes said, 'Among the English Poetry of the last half-century, Charles Causley's could well turn out to be the best loved and the most needed.' Apart from six years in the wartime Royal Navy he lived almost all his life in his native town of Launceston in Cornwall, where he also once worked as a teacher. He has published many collections of his work both for adults and for children and won a number of literary awards and prizes. In 1986 he was appointed CBE.

Timothy Winters

Timothy Winters comes to school
With eyes as wide as a football pool,
Ears like bombs and teeth like splinters:
A blitz of a boy is Timothy Winters.

His belly is white, his neck is dark,
And his hair is an exclamation mark.
His clothes are enough to scare a crow
And through his britches the blue winds blow.

When teacher talks he won't hear a word
And he shoots down dead the arithmetic-bird,
He licks the patterns off his plate
And he's not even heard of the Welfare State.

Timothy Winters has bloody feet
And he lives in a house on Suez Street,
He sleeps in a sack on the kitchen floor
And they say there aren't boys like him any more.

Old Man Winters likes his beer
And his missus ran off with a bombardier,
Grandma sits in the grate with a gin
And Timothy's dosed with an aspirin.

The Welfare Worker lies awake
But the law's as tricky as a ten-foot snake,
So Timothy Winters drinks his cup
And slowly goes on growing up.

At Morning Prayers the Master helves
For children less fortunate than ourselves,
And the loudest response in the room is when
Timothy Winters roars 'Amen!'

So come one angel, come on ten:
Timothy Winters says 'Amen
Amen amen amen amen.'
Timothy Winters, Lord.
     Amen.

I Love My Darling Tractor

I love my darling tractor,
love its merry din,
Its muscles made of iron and steel,
Its red and yellow skin.

I love to watch its wheels go round
However hard the day,
And from its bed inside the shed
It never thinks to stray.

It saves my arm, it saves my leg,
It saves my back from toil,
And it's merry as a skink when I give it a drink
Of water and diesel oil.

I love my darling tractor
As you can clearly see,
And so, the jolly farmer said,
Would you if you were me.

I am the Song

I am the song that sings the bird.
I am the leaf that grows the land.
I am the tide that moves the moon.
I am the stream that halts the sand.
I am the cloud that drives the storm.
I am the earth that lights the sun.
I am the fire that strikes the stone.
I am the clay that shapes the hand.
I am the word that speaks the man.

Early in the Morning

Early in the morning
The water hits the rocks,
The birds are making noises
Like old alarum clocks,
The soldier on the skyline
Fires a golden gun
And over the back of the chimney-stack
Explodes the silent sun.

I Had A Little Cat

I had a little cat called Tim Tom Tay,
I took him to town on market day,
I combed his whiskers, I brushed his tail,
I wrote on a label, 'Cat for Sale.
Knows how to deal with rats and mice.
Two pounds fifty. Bargain price.'

But when the people came to buy
I saw such a look in Tim Tom's eye
That it was clear as clear could be
I couldn't sell Tim for a fortune's fee.
I was shamed and sorry, I'll tell you plain,
And I took home Tim Tom Tay again.

Good Morning, Mr Croco-doco-dile

Good morning, Mr Croco-doco-dile,
And how are you today?
I like to see you croco-smoco-smile
In your croco-woco-way.

From the tip of your beautiful croco-toco-tail
To your croco-hoco-head
You seem to me so croco-stoco-still
As if you're coco-doco-dead.

Perhaps if I touch your croco-cloco-claw
Or your croco-snoco-snout,
Or get up close to your coco-joco-jaw
I shall very soon find out.

But suddenly I croco-soco-see
In your croco-oco-eye
A curious kind of croco-gloco-gleam,
So I just don't think I'll try.

Forgive me, Mr Croco-doco-dile
But it's time I was away.
Let's talk a little croco-woko-while
Another croco-doco-day.

All Day Saturday

Let it sleet on Sunday,
Monday let it snow,
Let the mist on Tuesday
From the salt-sea flow.
Let it hail on Wednesday,
Thursday let it rain,
Let the wind on Friday
Blow a hurricane,
But Saturday, Saturday
Break fair and fine
And all day Saturday
Let the sun shine.

Liz Brownlee

Liz Brownlee is an award-winning poet who performs her work with her assistance dogs, Lola and Paddy, in schools, libraries, literary and nature festivals. She has fun organizing poetry retreats, exhibitions and events, and runs the poetry website Poetry Roundabout. She is a National Poetry Day Ambassador, curates the blog and Twitter for Children's Poetry Summit, and has been shortlisted for the CLiPPA poetry prize.

Purrfect

A aaa A

When
you're
smitten by
a kitten, what's
your option?
one adoption.

Truth

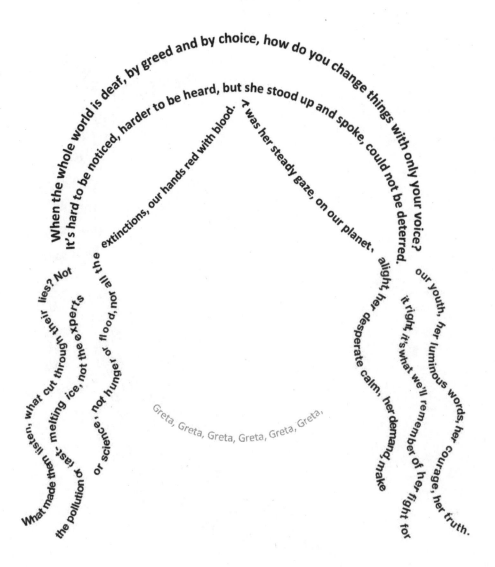

When the whole world is deaf, by greed and by choice, how do you change things with only your voice?

It's hard to be noticed, harder to be heard, but she stood up and spoke, could not be deterred.

Not all the extinctions, our hands red with blood. ↑ was her steady gaze, on our planet,

What made them listen, what cut through their lies? Not the experts, not melting ice, not the pollution or fast-or science, not hunger or flood, not alight, her desperate calm, her demand, make our youth, her luminous words, her courage, her truth. it right, it's what we'll remember of her fight for

Greta, Greta, Greta, Greta, Greta, Greta,

Narwhal

While starry night spins,
in sleek,
snow
flake
skins,
the uni-
corns fly,
tusks spiral
dizzily, clouds
skim the skies,
seas glitter by,
seeking out fish
shoals in oceans
of sea ice;
mysterious
and shy, they
trail threads
of silver
sew them-
selves to
into the
white sea and sky·

Slithering Silver

A shiny, slimy trail unravels behind each tiny snail tail's travels, without fail it's long and winding, though only one footprint's left behind him...

93

Blackbird

The blackbird **is**
a common bird,
a sleek shadow-feathered
boy, who sings out from a
golden bill, with little gaps
for joy. He lifts his voice when
rain has passed and washed the
garden clean, and drizzles notes
of loveliness upon the damp, lush
green. A summer sound, like
soaring lark, but clear and
true and strong, he whistles and
the world becomes
blackbird
blue sky
Song!

The Ghoul Inspectre's Coming

The Ghoul
Inspectre's coming,
dust off ● ● your lazy
bones, tidy out your coffins,
polish up your mournful moans.
Practise rib cage rattles, check that your chains
still clank, gibber when you're spoken to and keep your cell *ars dank.*
Display your bat collection and cobweb hanging
talents - freshen up the bloodstains, see
that the spook books balance.
Hover to attention, grease
your glides and brush
your mould - the
Ghoul Inspectre's
coming, make
sure his
welcome's
Cold!

Christmas Eve

Our
pud is
cooked,
meat stuffed and rolled –
smells drift of fruit and almonds where
the cake is iced and waiting.
Our tree is up, green, red and gold,
and twists of tinsel shimmer there
from lights illuminating.
Our foil-wrapped secrets to unfold,
and tiptoe stockings hung with care,
are all at once creating,
a feeling that we want to hold
suspended in the tingling air –
it's
Called
Anticipating

Matt Goodfellow

Matt Goodfellow is an award-winning poet from Manchester. His collections include: *Bright Bursts of Colour*, *Let's Chase Stars Together*, *Caterpillar Cake*, *Chicken on the Roof* and *Being Me*.

Start Now

be the change
you want to see
walk the walk
stand with me

take the challenge
spread the word
we can make
our voices heard

every single
action helps
with a friend
or by yourself

be the change
you want to see
walk the walk
stand with me

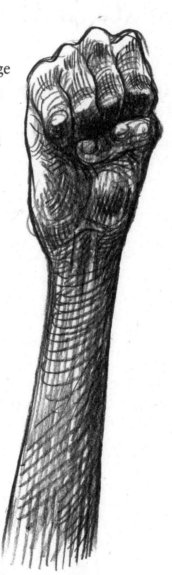

Messages

look closely and you'll find them
everywhere

in fields of patterned grasses
drafted by the hare

embroidered by the bluebells
through a wood

in scattered trails of blossom
stamped into the mud

scorched by heather-fire
across the moors

in looping snail-trails
scrawled on forest floors

scored across the sky
by screaming swifts

in rolling, twisting peaks
of drifting mountain mist

With the Waterfalls

I'm miles away today: I'm with the waterfalls.
I won't be round to play so please don't try to call.

I'm out beyond the boundary in the shimmer-spray.
Thick folds of mist surround me but I know the way.

I've walked towards the roar a thousand times before.
I'm miles away today: I'm with the waterfalls.

Each and Every One

dwi dynol
jeg er menneske
ako ay tao
he tangata ahau
jestem człowiekiem
i ahay aadanaha
ich bin menschlich
abụ m mmadụ
soy humano
sono umano
je suis humain
i am human

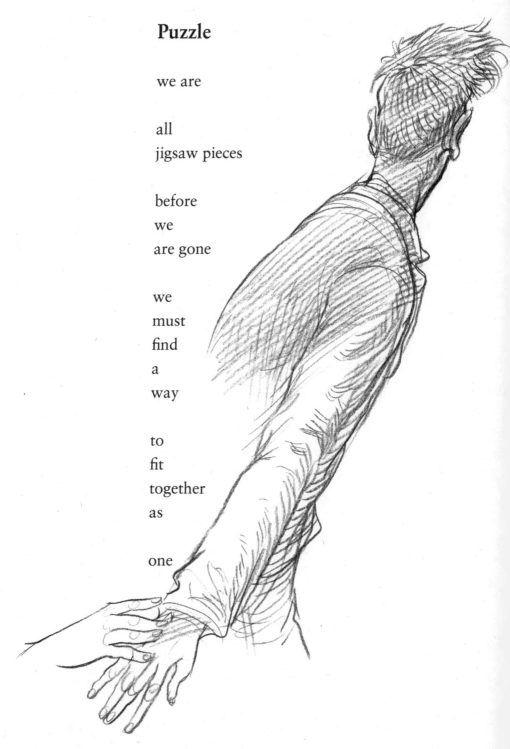

Puzzle

we are

all
jigsaw pieces

before
we
are gone

we
must
find
a
way

to
fit
together
as

one

Can't Take the Future Out of Me

can't take the stars out of the sky
can't take the story from a tree
can't take the moonlight from your eyes
can't take the future out of me

can't take the bark out of a dog
can't take the wildness from the sea
can't take the darkness from a dream
can't take the future out of me

can't take the sparkle from the frost
can't take the bumble from a bee
can't take the pride out of a smile
can't take the future out of me

Poem for a New Year

Something's moving in,
I hear the weather in the wind,
sense the tension of a sheep-field
and the pilgrimage of fins.

Something's not the same,
I taste the sap and feel the grain,
hear the rolling of the rowan
ringing, singing in a change.

Something's set to start,
there's meadow-music in the dark
and the clouds that shroud the mountain
slowly, softly start to part.

Laura Mucha

Laura Mucha is an ex-lawyer turned poet and author. Her writing has won multiple international awards and been featured on TV, radio and public transport, as well as in hospitals, hospices, prisons, books, magazines and newspapers around the world.

Her own children's books have been described as 'a must have for every school' by *The School Librarian* and 'stunningly original' by BookTrust.

When not writing, Laura spends her time visiting schools around the world and working with organisations such as the National Literacy Trust, Royal Society of Medicine and UNICEF to try to improve the lives of children.

Collage

I use my
 general purpose scissors
to cut brown card into small shards.
They have
 hard-wearing carbon blades
and slice precisely
to make the bark of an elm tree.
They are
 supplied in a smart PVC wallet
which I cut
to create a stream.
I tear some
 ivory tissue paper
to form cirrus clouds.
I crumple more
to add stratocumulus.
I stick this to
 versatile paper that's perfect for drawing and sketching
using
 traditional Japanese glue.
I give it to Dad, who puts it in
 a 120 gauge thick black sack
and tells me
to do something useful
for once.

Night Flight

Tonight I fancy a flight,
so I shuffle my short feathers
and jump.

Clusters of city lights
stretch, spread and sprawl
into sparkling starfish.

A whisper of clouds
tickles my feet.
A current lifts me like a leaf –

I float, I glide,
I hold my feathered wings out wide
and watch the world beneath.

The occasional plane passes.
The odd meteorite. Together,
we set the sky alight.

Flight is always best at night.

Listening To

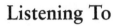

Brrrrrrrrrrrreeeeeeeeep
Iiiip iiiiip iiiiip
Raarp rarrp rarrp rarrp
Deecha deecha deecha
Ssshhh-chhh-chhh ssshhh-chhh-chhh
Ooooweepooweepooweep
Nndurrrrrr nndurrrrrr
Gyaaaaayk gyaaaaayk

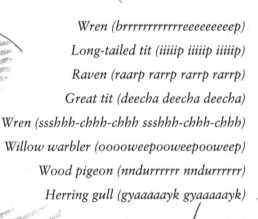

Wren (brrrrrrrrrrrreeeeeeeeeep)
Long-tailed tit (iiiiip iiiiip iiiiip)
Raven (raarp rarrp rarrp rarrp)
Great tit (deecha deecha deecha)
Wren (ssshhh-chhh-chhh ssshhh-chhh-chhh)
Willow warbler (oooweepooweepooweep)
Wood pigeon (nndurrrrrr nndurrrrrr)
Herring gull (gyaaaaayk gyaaaaayk)

Fleming's Petri Dish

Alexander Fleming wasn't the most hygienic scientist, and
when he went on holiday in 1928, he didn't clean up his petri
dishes. When he returned, he discovered a gloop that had
created a bacteria-free circle around itself. In other words,
the gloop (the 'juice' from the Penicillium notatum fungus)
destroyed bacteria. Fleming called the active substance
penicillin, and it was developed into the first ever antibiotic.
Even if you haven't been saved by penicillin or another
antibiotic, one of your ancestors probably was.
This poem is based on the original petri dish.

Compliments Of Shakespeare

A poem inspired by Shakespeare's insults

You poisonous, slimy, bunch-backed toad,
you coward, beggar, shallow rogue –
your villainous smell offends my nose!
You're rank, you make me sick.

You elvish, starveling, stinky hog,
if only you'd been born a dog
I'd like you more.
But no. Instead, you're like a sore,
you're like a boil I'd like to pop.
You're speaking but I wish you'd stop.

You're lily-livered, knotty, proud,
your February face is full of cloud –
you're lumpy, foul, all froth and scum.
I have to say I think your bum
is the best thing about you.

You're Never Too . . .

You're never too poor to give away kindness,
you're never too rich to feel sadness or fear,
you're never too quiet to make others listen,
you're never too loud to stop and to hear.

You're never too guilty to ask for forgiveness,
you're never too flawless to need help to cope,
you're never too big to feel ever-so-tiny,
you're never too little to give someone hope.

You're never too foolish to try to be wiser,
you're never too wise to need time to heal,
you're never too this or too that to make changes,
you're never too young to say how you feel.

I'm An Orchestra

Today I am the double bass,
solid, sonorous, strong.
I'm going somewhere, things to do,
always driving on.

But sometimes I'm the cor anglais,
solitary, subdued.
If my tone is wistful,
it's my melancholy mood.

Sometimes I'm the trumpet,
a spicy, strident sound,
others the euphonium,
velvety and round.

I'm the triangle, worth the wait,
I'm the chimes, I captivate,
I'm the cymbals, clang and crash,
I'm a bass drum, meet your match,
I'm crotales, decisive, sure,
I'm the tam-tam.
    Hear. My. **Roar.**

I'm an orchestra.

Dom Conlon

Dom is a disabled, hat-wearing, thought-thinking, cake-eating poet and author whose books have been nom nom nominated (sorry, still thinking about cake there) for the Carnegie and the Greenaway medals. He's a bit of a work in progress but has written books such as *Meet Matilda Rocket Builder*, *This Rock That Rock* and the Wild Wanderers series. The books (not him) have been praised by Chris Riddell, Brian Bilston, Nicola Davies, Robin Ince and even the European Space Agency, so that's a bit smashing. His poetry has appeared in *Wonder*, *We Wish You A Merry Christmas* and many other tip-top anthologies.

how stars die

she sits on the bench
feeding the birds late into the evening
with two coats a scarf and a hat
to keep her warm
as her shoulders sag
and her bright eye dims
because this is how stars die

as her children's children's children
shiver and look and think
how did we not notice
for a thousand years or more
and how cold we are without her
and how dark the house is now
because this is how stars are mourned

until her winter garden blooms once more
a youthful rose of memories
blushing the sky and laying to rest
the myth that age must weary
and rage must die
and stories stop
and endings can't be
beginnings

because this is how stars are born

Quietly Remarkable

You're never first
You're sometimes last
And lessons don't
Sink in so fast.
It feels as though
Your other mates
Are quick to speak
In class debates
But you're the Moon
And that's ok
You're doing fine
You're here to stay
Quietly remarkable.

You look ahead
But nothing's clear,
Every choice
Is edged with fear.
You don't know what
You'd like to do,
The jobs you see
Don't feel quite you
But you're the Moon
And that's ok
You're doing fine
You're here to stay
Quietly remarkable.

You're doing good
When that one friend
Turns to you
In the end
And you're right there
To help them out
To show them what
The world's about
Because you see it
Through your eyes
And no-one else
Can be as wise
And quietly remarkable

Cos you're the Moon
And that's ok
You're doing fine
You're here to stay
Quietly remarkable.

The Way Planets Talk

What might we hear if we listened
for the star-forged language
the planets used when sound was new
and words had no full stops?

We might hear the distant vowels
of Neptune, each word as long
as life, each sun-abandoned syllable
the sound of a breathing whale.

We might hear the soft lilt of Uranus,
with its dictionary of duck eggs
plopped into blue flour – a thousand
definitions in a single air-thrown sigh.

We might hear the singing voice of Saturn,
with its billion letter alphabet
scattered along a single groove,
its voice recorded in a tantrum of sentences.

We might hear the whirling words of Jupiter,
where 'hello' is the oil in an engine
and 'I love you' is the red echo
of a candle flame dying at sunrise.

We might once have even heard Mars
utter its own name before the words dried
on the tip of its burnt tongue, before
a final, thirst-silenced cry scratched the dust.

We might hear Venus,
Venus who speaks in a dialect
separated from our own
only by a dream on a too-warm night.

And nestled between stone-fist silences
we might hear Mercury
wailing like a boiled baby
each time the sun scrubs its face.

If we listened we might hear these planets,
and take the language from their molten cores
and learn that distance is a comma,
a pause in how we talk about tomorrow.

Bentback

I heard every word when I was nine:
Bentback. Bentback. Look at him. Bentback.
I heard every word when I was being bullied
for having a back as twisted as a question mark.
I heard every word and I stood and I said
that soon I'll have a spine of steel,
that soon the doctors would break me then make me
new again,
that soon they'd core me like an apple
and fill me with nectar
from the garden of Eden
and that soon I'd be unbreakable
unshakable, a thing carved
from beneath a mountain
with veins of magma,
a thing able to cause earthquakes
with a cough and storms
with a sneeze and that then then
they'd know how a bad word felt
when it was deflected and reflected back
with the power of science.

And I'm laughing now because I know this:
I know I held them there before me
not with fists or fear but with a voice.
And though I stood there reliant on doctors
I was defiant by myself.
And there and then I put a lid on any kid
I'd care to, who'd dare to tell me what was normal
and I showed them all
how lucky I was because
even though my body's crashing
I had a voice like rivers smashing
and that a back as twisted as a question mark means
I'm always enquiring
searching for inspiring
with a heart that's never tiring.
And guess what?
They heard
every word.

Swift by your side

Circle as you sleep, my love
and drift upon your dreams.
Ruling from the clouds, my love
is simpler than it seems.

Be queen above the world, my love
be the king who's free to fly.
Let the wealth within your wings, my love
be scattered in the sky.

The kingdom of your eye, my love
is measured by the sun.
The journey to my heart, my love
begins when that is done.

I hear your piper's call, my love
the poetry of tears.
I'll follow where you lead, my love
as months turn into years.

And when we go to ground, my love
when all our wings are old.
We'll gaze up to the blue, my love
and count our words of gold.

Draw Me

Who drew the grin of an invisible cat?
Who drew the cost of the maddest hat?

Who drew the tea in the party scene?
Who drew the rage on a red-faced queen?

Who drew the girl from tall to small?
Who drew the grump of an egg on a wall?

Who drew the fights of fat twin boys?
Who drew the jam that a mouse enjoys?

Who drew the trick of a rabbit's clock?
Who drew the burble of a Jabberwock?

Who drew the smoke of an insect's pipe?
Who drew the mushroom nice and ripe?

Who drew the old man upside down?
Who drew the sparkle of a golden crown?

Who drew the book which became perennial?
A man by the name of Sir John Tenniel.

Seeing

And that wall and that wall
and that wall and that and

you didn't realise they had cracks
delicate as a baby's veins

most prominent when the sun
remembers it is daytime

each thread an act of kindness
tiny on its own like the sound

of a gift or a food parcel
kissing the step

or the first words you spoke
after he had died before you realised

there are people
who will listen

people who will reach you
people who will teach you

those cracks can bring down walls
those acts of kindness can be calls

for change

and that crack and that crack
and that crack and that and

our bodies are not built from stone
but made to change made to heal

made to feel for sun on the skin
food in the stomach voices in the air

not money in the bank
or divisions of sexracefaith just

tiny acts of kindness
delicate as the first roots you grew

after the old world died.

Coral Rumble

Coral Rumble is a popular, award-winning poet who has loved being part of the Macmillan family. She has worked as a poet and performer for many years, and has visited numerous schools to juggle words with children of all ages. She has even taught some teachers to word juggle!

Coral won the Caterpillar Poetry Prize, 2018, and her winning poem, 'Mustafa's Jumper', was published as a story. Her latest collection of poems, *Riding a Lion* was shortlisted for the North Somerset Teachers' Book Awards. A new collection, *Things That Should be in a Poem*, is out soon

Her greatest fan is Gus, her dog, who gives her unconditional love – as long as she keeps buying dog treats.

Black Cat Remembers an Ancient Tale

Black Cat – inky, leaping shadow –
Lands on a wall cushioned with moss.
She sits, she stares, she waits,
Comfortable with her own company.

She looks at the moon and remembers a tale
About a cow jumping over it,
About a small dog laughing.
She muses on how a dog should never laugh,
About how dogs do not deserve happiness.
There was a cat in the ancient tale, though,
A brilliant cat of outstanding musical ability.
She recalls how a dish ran away with a spoon –
She doesn't know why, but the cat didn't get involved,
Which must mean it was an unimportant detail.

Black Cat's ears twitch, her sleek head turns
As a breeze pushes a parched leaf from the wall.
There's a smell of burnt hickory in the air, and
Over the wall, the church clock strikes 1.
Black Cat jumps, instinctively knows a mouse will run by.
The patterns of stories reside in her bones.

Fish Under Ice

We step through snow,
my little brother
filling my footprints
with his own wellied feet.

The small hollow in our garden
cups the pond in its icy hands,
surrounds the fish under ice
with reeds as stiff as castle walls.

We brush the glassy water
with mittened hands,
pour warm water
to melt the frost
that clouds
the pane.

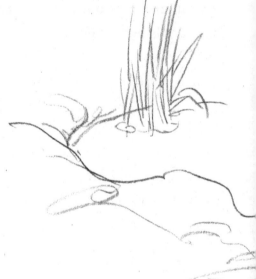

Then we see them –
the flick of a tale,
the gold of a scale,
drifting slowly like
ghostly submarines.

And my brother,
full of questions, asks,
'Can they breathe?
Are they cold?
Do they sleep?
Can I hold?'

But I just wonder
at their patience,
as they wait for
sunshine and
a warm breeze
that whispers,
'The spring will come,
the spring will come.'

A Seasonal High

Football focus
Match of the Day
That's what I call
A proper Saturday
Goal posts, nets
Corner flags flapping
Beads of sweat
(A manager sacking)
New kits gleaming
In the autumn sun
New star signings
Out to stun
Outstretched banners
Chanting voices
Player lists
(Some dodgy choices)
Commentators
Losing the plot
Referees pointing
To the spot
Driving rain
Against the stand
Random notes
From a makeshift band
Whistle shrills
And crossbar smacks,
My smile is wide
Now football's back.

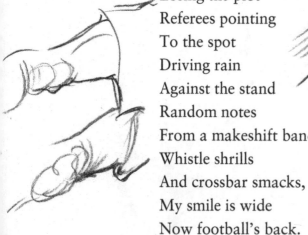

Bright Sparks

y

a

w

a

t

a

o

l

f

t

a

h

t

s

k

r

a

p

s

of
to let go
they're forced
spit and hiss as
lose their splintered grip,
but clawing, wooden fingers
hums a tune of destruction -
crackles a cackle of hot delight
holds tightly with its orange glow,
the furnace heart of the fire consumes -

Siblings

I remember when we gathered sticks,
And stood on the stone bridge over
The busy stream that sliced between
The field on the left and
The farm on the right.

The race was on.
Stick after stick
Disappeared
Reappeared
Disappeared
Reappeared,
And Dad would clap,
But always said, 'It doesn't matter who wins.'

I almost believed him back then –
That coming first didn't matter,
That it was the taking part that counted,
That fun was the thing,
That only willingness was required.

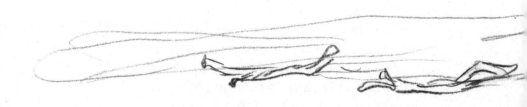

But from that day, the race was on
As my brother and I competed
For Dad's attention, for his applause –
We measured each accomplishment
By the width of his smile.

And his approval,
His pride, has
Disappeared
Reappeared
Disappeared
Reappeared,
As he continues to clap
A bit louder for the son who comes first.

Sometimes

A cinquain

Sometimes
They just stare hard
Nudge each other and smile,
And I pretend that I don't care –
Sometimes

Street Lights

The town leapt a little, tonight,
As the Christmas lights came on.
Everyday streets became more important
And even the darkest pathways glistened.
Stars and snowflakes
Angels and reindeer
Flashed and flickered a holy-white whisper,
Making our town,
Our ordinary, brick and tarmac town,
Sparkle like a frosted castle
In a far-off, frozen land.

James Carter

Ever met an alien? Award-winning poet, non-fiction writer and musician JAMES WINSTON HENRY CARTER (stop sniggering) is probably the closest you'll ever get. Where does he get his ideas from? The magic wood at the back of his house – obvs.

James travels to schools all over the cosmos with his melodica (that's Steve) and ukulele (that's Erik) to run VERY lively, creative and inspiring poetry and music days with the express intention of GETTING HUMAN CHILDREN WRITING.

An ambassador for National Poetry Day, James says that when he grows up (he won't) he wants to see a wolf and a puffin and a dung beetle in the wild. Oh yes, and a woolly mammoth too.

LoveYouMore

Do I love you
to the moon and back?
No I love you
more than that

I love you to the desert sands
the mountains, stars
the planets and

I love you to the deepest sea
and deeper still
through history

Before beyond I love you then
I love you now
I'll love you when

The sun's gone out
the moon's gone home
and all the stars are fully grown

When I no longer say these words
I'll give them to the winds, the birds
so that they will still be heard

    I

        love

            you

Take a Poem

Why not take a poem
wherever you go?
pop it in your pocket
nobody will know

Take it to your classroom
stick it on the wall
tell them all about it
read it in the hall

Take it to the bathroom
tuck it up in bed
take the time to learn it
keep it in your head

Take it for a day trip
take it on a train
fold it as a hat
when it starts to rain

Take it to a river
fold it as a boat
pop it on the water
hope that it will float

Take it to a hilltop
fold it as a plane
throw it up skywards
time and time again

Take it to a post box
send it anywhere
out into the world
with
    tender
        loving
            care

Electric Guitars

I like electric guitars :
played mellow or moody
frantic or fast - on CDs
or tapes, at home or in
cars – live in the streets
at gigs or in bars.
I like
electric
guitars :
played
choppy
like
reggae
or angry
like
rock or
chirpy
like
jazz or
strummy
like
pop or
heavy
like
metal - it
bothers
me not.
I like electric guitars :
their strings and their straps
and their wild wammy bars - their
jangling and twanging and funky
wah-wahs - their fuzz boxes,
frets and multi-effects -
pick-ups, machine
heads, mahogany necks
- their plectrums, their wires,
and big amplifiers. I like electric
guitars : played loudly, politely - dully
or brightly - daily or nightly - badly
or nicely. I like electric guitars :
bass, lead and rhythm -
I basically dig 'em -
I like elect
r
i
c
g
u
i
t
a
r
s

How Easily

the present
escapes into the past.
Like raindrops on a lake,

like moths into the dark.
That afternoon you learnt
to swim. The night

you tried to count
the stars. Ever passing
through your hands,

moments disappear
like sand. So catch them.
Trap them. Write them

down. Preserve them
as your memories.
Turn them into

words
      like
            these.

The Moon Speaks!

I, the moon,
would like it known – I
never follow people home. I
simply do not have the time. And
neither do I ever shine. For what you
often see at night is me reflecting solar
light. And I'm not cheese . . . ! No, none of
these: no mozzarellas, cheddars, bries, all
you'll find here – if you please – are my
dusty, empty seas. And cows do not
jump over me. Now that is simply
lunacy! You used to come and
visit me. Oh do return,
I'm lonely, see.

See it Like a Poet
... with 20-20 vision.

Where
    imagery
meets rhythm.

Syllabic repetition.
    New ways
to look and listen.

To let your reader
        view the world
    through the windows
of your words.

So don't just
    tell it.
Show it.

See it
    like a
poet.

This Is Where . . .

. . . I learned to be.
And this is where I learned to read,
and write and count and act in plays,
and blossom in so many ways . . .

And this is where I learned to sing,
express myself, and really think.
And this is where I learned to dream,
to wonder why and what things mean.

And this is where I learned to care,
to make good friends, to give, to share,
to kick, to catch, to race, to run.
This is where I had such fun.

And this is where I grew and grew.
And this is where? My primary school.

Valerie Bloom

Valerie Bloom was born in Orange Hill, Jamaica, grew up in the nearby town of Frankfield, and came to England in 1979. She studied English with African and Caribbean Studies at the University of Kent at Canterbury from 1982 to 1984. In 1995 the same university awarded her an Honorary Masters Degree for her work as a poet.

Her poems have been published in over 200 adult and children's anthologies.

She has been a librarian, a teacher, a steel-band instructor and an arts officer. She now writes, performs and conducts workshops full-time. Her most recent collection Stars with Flaming Tails won CLiPPA 2022.

Pinda Cake

De pinda cake lady comin' down,
With her basket an' glass case she comin' to town,
She stop by the school gate an' set up her stall,
An' while she a-set up hear de old lady bawl:

Pinda! Pinda cake!
Pinda! Pinda cake!
Gal an' bwoy me jus' done bake,
Come buy yuh lovely pinda cake!

She have grater cake an' she have duckunoo'
Coconut drops an' bulla cake too,
Jackass corn an' plantain tart,
But the t'ing dat dearest to me heart

Is *Pinda! Pinda cake!*
Pinda! Pinda cake!
Gal an' bwoy me jus' done bake,
Come buy yuh lovely pinda cake!

We all crowd round her an' yuh can tell
By de look o' de cake dem, an' de spicy smell
Dat they won't stay in de glass case too long,
As we buy from de lady, we join in the song.

Pinda! Pinda cake!
Pinda! Pinda cake!
Gal an' bwoy me jus' done bake,
Come buy yuh lovely pinda cake!

Frost

Overnight, a giant spilt icing sugar on the ground,
He spilt it on the hedgerows, and the trees without a sound,
He made a wedding cake of the haystack in the field,
He dredged the countryside and the grass was all concealed,
He sprinkled sugar on the roofs, in patches not too neat,
And in the morning when we woke, the world around was sweet.

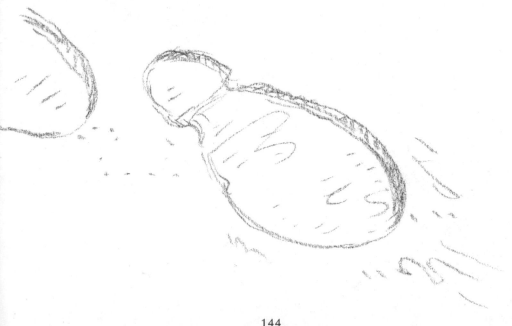

How to Ask for a Hamster

Mum, can I keep a snake in my room?
What did you say? Are you mad?
Well, Jamie keeps a snake in *his* room,
He got it from his dad.

Will you buy me a mongoose, Mum?
I've played with one; it belongs to Maria,
It's really docile; can I please, Mum?
I don't think that's a good idea!

Can I have a pony then?
I could afford to pay for hay.
D'you know how much a pony costs?
Japhet got one for *his* birthday.

How about a crocodile?
They sell them in Didcot,
I think that's where Chloe bought hers.
Can I have one? *Certainly not!*

I'll settle for a tarantula then,
It would be in a cage, of course.
Joshua has a tarantula.
Oh no! I can think of nothing worse!

What about a little monkey?
Tina has a chimpanzee.
Everyone in class has a pet,
Everybody except me.

You can have a cat or a hamster,
You cannot have a snake or a mouse.
No crocs, monkey or creepy-crawlies,
I won't have a zoo in this house.

OK, I'll settle for a hamster,
It's better than nothing, I suppose.
Oh, there's the bell, must be Jamie,
We promised to go and play at Joe's.

Jamie, you were right, I tried it,
Just like you said, it worked a treat,
I'm getting the hamster, now tell me
How do I ask for a parakeet?

Haircut Rap

Ah sey, ah want it short,
Short back an' side,
Ah tell him man, ah tell him
When ah teck him aside,
Ah sey, ah want a haircut
Ah can wear with pride,
So lef' it long on top
But short back an' side.

Ah sey try an' put a pattern
In the shorter part,
Yuh could put a skull an' crossbone,
Or an arrow through a heart,
Meck sure ah have enough hair lef'
Fe cover me wart,
Lef' a likkle pon the top,
But the res' – keep it short.

Well, bwoy, him start to cut
An' me settle down to wait,
Him was cuttin' from seven
Till half-past eight,
Ah was startin' to get worried
'Cause ah see it gettin' late,
But then him put the scissors down
Sey, 'There yuh are, mate.'

Well ah did see a skull an' a
Criss-cross bone or two,
But was me own skull an' bone
That was peepin' through
Ah look jus' like a monkey
Ah did see once at the zoo,
Him sey, 'What's de matter, Tammy,
Don't yuh like the hair-do?'

Well, ah feel me heart stop beatin'
When ah look pon me reflection,
Ah feel like somet'ing frizzle up
Right in me middle section
Ah look aroun' fe somewhey
Ah could crawl into an' hide
The day ah mek me brother cut
Me hair short back an' side.

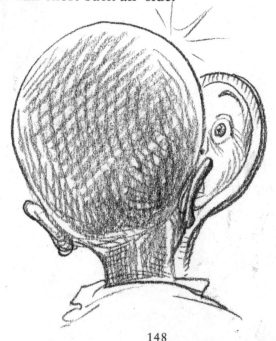

Fruits

Half a pawpaw in the basket
Only one o' we can have it,
Wonder which one that will be?
I have a feeling that is me.

One guinep up in the tree
Hanging down there tempting me
It don't mek no sense to pick it,
One guinep can't feed a cricket.

Two ripe guava pon the shelf,
I know I hide them there meself,
When night come an' it get dark
Me an' them will have a talk.

Three sweet-sop, well I jus' might
Give one o' them a nice big bite,
Cover up the bite jus' so, sis,
Then no one will ever notice.

Four red apple near me chair,
Who so careless put them there?
Them don't know how me love apple?
Well, thank God fe silly people.

Five jew-plum, I can't believe it!
How they know jew-plum's me fav'rit?
But why they hide them in the cupboard?
Cho, people can be so awkward.

Six naseberry, you want a nibble?
Why baby must always dribble?
Come wipe you mout', it don't mek sense
To broadcast the evidence.

Seven mango! What a find
The smaddy who lef them really kind,
One fe you an' six fe me,
If you want more, climb the tree.

Eight orange fe cousin Clem,
But I have just one problem,
How to get rid o' the eight skin
That the orange them come in.

Nine jackfruit! Not even me
Can finish nine, but let me see,
I don't suppose that they will miss one,
That was hard, but now me done.

Ten banana, mek them stay,
I feeling really full today,
Mek me lie down on me bed, quick,
Lawd, ah feeling really sick.

Christmas is Here

When the fee-fees start to bloom
Purple and white,
When the days begin to be
Shorter than night,
When the poinsettia's leaves
Turn from green to red,
When the turkey in the coop
Starts to look well-fed,
When we dig the yellow yams,
And pick the gungo peas,
When the tall, white, cane-flags
Start waving in the breeze,
When oranges and tangerines
Start to fill the baskets
Of the people on their way
To the different markets,
When the fruits which have been dried
Are soaking in the wine,
When the fat green cho-chos hang
Heavy from the vine,
When we look out on the fields
To the red bulbs of sorrel,
When the pickled meats come out
From their place in the brine barrel,
When each meal contains a slice
Of avocado pear,
Then we know for certain that
Christmas-time is here.

Autumn Gilt

The late September sunshine
Lime green on the linden leaves
Burns bronze on the slated roof-tops,
Yellow on the farmer's last sheaves.
It flares flame-like on the fire hydrant,
Is ebony on the blackbird's wing,
Blue beryl on the face of the ocean,
Glints gold on the bride's wedding ring.
A sparkling rainbow on the stained-glass window,
It's a silver sheen on the kitchen sink,
The late September sunshine
Is a chameleon, I think.

John Rice

John Rice is a Scottish poet who has been writing poems since he was 10 years old. He is now 74. So he certainly has written a big bundle of bouncy poems! Most of John's poems for children are published by Macmillan and many have been broadcast on television and radio. He loves writing poems about space and astronomy. John has performed for children in hundreds of schools and has even made forty-six teachers laugh.

Constant, Constant, Little Light

*A twenty-first-century version of Jane Taylor's poem
'The Star', now universally known as the nursery rhyme
'Twinkle, Twinkle, Little Star'.*

Constant, constant, little light,
catch my eye in darkest night.
What can speed so fast, so high,
laser-like across the sky?

When the sleepy sun has set
and the night has cast her net,
It's then your orbit forms a ring,
round the earth a song to sing.

Constant, constant, little light,
I know you're a satellite.

Cruising, spinning, seldom seen,
beaming pictures to our screens.
Weather-watching, tracking storms,
plotting maps and all life forms.

Scanning, spying from above,
are you hawk or are you dove?
Silent, stealthy space-age Thor,
armed with weapons for a real star war.

From your tiny, silver glow,
who can tell what wrongs may flow?
But for now I hold you bright,
constant, constant, little light.

Constant, constant, little light,
I know you're a satellite.

Driving at Night with My Dad

Open the window,
the cool summer night swooshes in.
My favourite music playing loud.

2 a.m. – summer's midnight –
neither of us can sleep
so we go for a night drive.

Stars crowd the sky
and twinkle at us in code.
Our headlights reply in light-language.

A fox crosses, red and grey,
and arches under a fence:
rabbits run and a farm cat's eyes
catch our beam.
She stares at us for a second of stretched time . . .
. . . her eyes two new coins.

Through villages that are asleep,
past farms that are warm,
past houses that are dreaming,
under trees that are resting,
past birds that have no flight, no song.

I sense I am in some other country
where day, time, people no longer matter.
In this huge dark,
through the somewhere and the nowhere
of this uninhabited world,
I feel safe and secure
driving at night with my dad.

Low Owl

Cold morn: on fork of two o'clock
owl's hoot flows from hood of wood.

Owl's song rolls from blood to brood,
owl's hoot loops on to top of town roofs,
owl's song swoops on strong doors.

Owl's slow whoop – long, forlorn –
soft flood of moon song.

*This poem is a univocalic, which means that it uses
only one of the five vowels; in this case the vowel 'o'.*

Sounds Amazing

The **vrooommm** of a jet as it lands at Gatwick,
the **yaarrhhh** of a striker scoring his hatrick.

The **huurrmm** of a laptop as it warms up the tabletop,
the **truumm** of the traffic passing through Mablethorpe.

The **krirp** that you hear turning newspaper pages,
The **grraahhh** of the wild things escaping from cages.

The **whaarr** of the wind thrust out by propellers,
the **plirps** of light rain as it plops on umbrellas.

The **whoogly-whoog-whoo** of a common pigeon,
The **purring-pray-purr** as people practise religion.

The **tingly-tinks** of the Space Station antenna,
The **swushery-swish** when dancers waltz in Vienna.

Climbing the World

Heading home, the faces
of the passengers opposite
are reflected dark blue
in the late-night train windows.

I doze, my daughter yawns.

The head of the sleeping man
next to me lolls about like a puppet's.
His paperback slips from his lap
and falls on to the orange peel
he discarded before falling asleep.

He wakes in time to get off at Sevenoaks.

I pick up the book, brush the peel off the jacket.
It's *The Diary of a Young Girl: Anne Frank*,
the '97 Penguin edition, due back
at Paddington Library by 13 Dec.
I start reading the foreword

. . . Anne Frank kept a diary . . .

Her father, Otto Frank, edited her diaries
after she was dead.
I see him crying at the typewriter.

My daughter is twenty-seven.
We have great times together.
She is my friend and I love her.
Even in a train's harsh light she is very beautiful.
She is climbing the world.

Anne and Otto Frank
have taught me how to tell you this.

I shall now return the sleeping man's
book to Paddington Library.

Castle to be Built in the Woods

1.   Choose a wood.

2.   Make a clearing
near a stream.

3.   Dig a moat.
Make it deep, wide.
Fill it with water. One bridge only.

4.   Lay solid foundations for your castle.
Then build strong buttresses, stout keeps
and tall towers with crenellations
around the high battlements.

5.   Make sure your castle has servants such as
clerks, tailors, nurses, messengers,
damsels, brewers, and a barber.
You will need to lay down stores
of food, wine, wax, spices and herbs.

6.   An airy church inside the castle grounds
and a dark dungeon deep below ground
will mean that you can have
Heaven and Hell at your fingertips.
Don't forget to stock your arsenal with
swords, daggers, lances, shields, battleaxes, etc.

7. Fire arrows at anyone who tries to
   attack your castle. Build murder-holes
   so that you can drop missiles and stones
   on the heads of your enemies.
   If you catch spies, lock them in
   the smallest, narrowest, smelliest room.
   Act ruthlessly. Behead people, frequently.

8. Hide treasure in a very secret part of the castle.
   Lock a beautiful princess in the tower.
   Force your fiercest dragon to guard both of these.
   Nominate a knight who will fight your battles
   so that you are never injured or endangered.
   Employ a story-teller to make up tall tales
   and ghost stories about your castle.
   Marry someone and he can be the king.

A Minute to Midnight

A minute to midnight
and all is still.

For example, these are things that are still:
ornaments, coins, lamp-posts,
the cooker, Major Clark's Home for old folk
(just opposite our house, which is also still),
the newsagent's, a hut, soap, tractors,
freshly ironed trousers draped over the chair.

A minute to midnight
and all is still
except for the things that are moving.

Like, for example,
rivers, clouds, leaves, flags,
creaky windmills, lungs, birds' feathers,
digital clocks, grass, the wind,
non-sleeping animals (especially wolves),
planet Earth, the moon, satellites in space,
toenails (well they grow, don't they),
videos that are set to record
programmes in the middle of the night,
washing lines,
mobiles above babies' cots –
and babies' eyelids, they always flicker.

Kate Wakeling

Kate Wakeling is a poet and a musicologist (which means she finds out about music then writes about it). Kate loves writing poems that play with the sound and meaning of words, and that are full of both mischief and feeling. Kate's first collection of children's poetry, *Moon Juice*, won the 2017 CLiPPA prize and was nominated for the 2018 CILIP Carnegie Medal. Her second collection, *Cloud Soup*, was a book of the month in *The Guardian* and *The Scotsman* and has been shortlisted for the 2022 CLiPPA prize. Her poems for children have appeared in lots of excellent Macmillan books, including *A Poet for Every Day of the Year*, *Poems for 7 Year Olds*, *Poems for 8 Year Olds*, *Shaping the World* and *The Best Ever Book of Funny Poems*. Kate is a longstanding champion of guinea pigs and an enthusiastic player of Balinese gamelan music.

Word Hoard

Long ago,
when people laid straw on their floors,
and played football with pigs' bladders
and stuck leeches on the legs of the sick,
long *long* ago –
well, they made word hoards.

A word hoard is a set of words
with a certain magic about them.
They're words that stir the spirit
and tingle on the tongue.

A word hoard is a secret stash of vocab
that makes your heart hum.

Now, you might like a word
for its sound
or for its sense.

Or you might like a word
for both its music *and* its meaning,
like . . . *picnic* perhaps?

In any case,
what you put in your word hoard
is up to you.

Here's mine:

quick	tendril	magic	feast
root	music	weird	fierce
thirst	blossom	curse	drift
bright	worm	wander	sleep

What words,
I wonder,
might you keep
in yours?

Free

and we will open all the doors
and we will jump on all the beds
and we will leap from mountain top to mountain top
and we will laugh until we think we might explode
and we will laugh especially in those moments when we
    aren't really supposed to
and we will of course find this only makes the laughing a
    million times more extreme
and we will talk to animals
and we will stride across oceans
and we will dance like maniacs
and we will lie on the sofa watching TV with our shoes on
    because why not
and we will have long baths/short baths/no baths delete as
    applicable
and we will eat delicious foods
and we will not eat any of the bits we don't really like
and we will talk while lying on our backs and looking at the
    sky
and we will say the first thing that pops into our heads
and we will be always with our friends even when we are not
and we will smile with smiles so deep they make our eyes
    disappear
and we will grow wings
and we will
and we will
and we will

Comet

To be read as quickly as possible, in as few breaths as you can manage.

I'm a spinning, winning, tripping, zipping, super-sonic ice
queen:
see my moon zoom, clock my rocket, watch me splutter
tricksy space-steam.

I'm the dust bomb, I'm the freeze sneeze, I'm the top galactic
jockey
made (they think) of gas and ice and mystery bits of
something rocky.

Oh I sting a sherbet orbit, running rings round star or planet;
should I shoot too near the sun, my tail hots up: *ouch* –
OUCH – please fan it!

And I'm told I hold the answer to the galaxy's top question:
that my middle's made of history (no surprise I've indigestion)

but for now I sprint and skid and whisk and bolt and belt
and bomb it;
I'm that hell-for-leather, lunging, plunging, helter-skelter
COMET.

The Spy Café

The Spy Café's a peculiar place.

The sign on the door only ever says CLOSED.

They keep the lighting way down low
and the menu's written in invisible ink.

The special of the day is usually Spy Pie
(with the filling kept TOP SECRET).

No one has *ever seen the cook*.

The spies don't say much,
preferring to ink coded messages on napkins
and leave them casually on the other spies' plates.

The waiters wear wigs and dark glasses.

They mutter things like

      the badger is in the hole

to nobody in particular.

I'd suggest we meet for a cup of tea
but the Spy Café can be difficult to find.

Very difficult to find.

Very, very difficult to find.

Paean (or Eleven Uses for a Garden Pea)

1.   Frog football.
2.   One-third replacement for a miniature traffic light.
3.   Temporary emerald for edible ring.
4.   Environmentally-friendly clown's nose.
5.   Ocean-free planet.
6.   False eye for short-sighted lizard.
7.   Nostril filler.
8.   Spiller of a perfume fresher than newly-mown grass.
9.   Cannonball for the Grasshopper Army (THEY'RE COMING).
10.   Pesky tester of princesses.
11.   Trainee lime.

The Water in the Glass You Are Holding Right Now*

has led a million lives.
It has survived.

Perhaps a splash or two
dashed once or twice
across Niagara Falls.

Or lay locked in the ice
of the first snowball you threw.

Or you'll discover
this water once washed the hands of your
great-great-great-grandmother.

Maybe it powered the leaves
of your favourite tree.

Or once was brewed as tea
or (forgive me)
kangaroo wee.

* Feel free to fetch one.

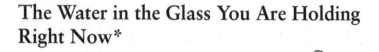

172

Perhaps it held the drops
that quenched the thirst
of the very first
triceratops.

Water goes nowhere and everywhere.
Water knows everything.

So it's not such a leap
to think
you hold in your hand
a link
to every kind of wildness,
to every kind of person.

Drink deep.

THE INSTRUCTIONS

1. How to spot THE INSTRUCTIONS

THE INSTRUCTIONS come in all shapes and sizes.
They are often found in and around:

- *Tall buildings with statues of lions outside*
- *Faces with an angry expression*
- *Faces with a smile seen only in the mouth
  but (crucially) not in the eyes*

2. The other instructions

There are plenty of *other* sorts of instructions,
which can of course be useful.
For example:

- *Try not to insert any part of your body into
  this pond: it contains an irritated crocodile*
- *For best results, keep both eyes open while
  landing this lopsided helicopter*
- *Do not under any circumstances eat the
  angry man's sandwich*

3. What THE INSTRUCTIONS want

You see, THE INSTRUCTIONS aren't here to help you.
They want to help someone or something else.

THE INSTRUCTIONS say things like:

- *No one's ever done THAT before: it CAN'T be a good idea*
- *Please do the SAME thing as all those OTHER people over THERE*
- *Hear that person talking in the PARTICULARLY loud voice? They must DEFINITELY be RIGHT.*

4. If you follow THE INSTRUCTIONS

If you follow THE INSTRUCTIONS it is unlikely anyone
will ever be very cross with you.
If you follow THE INSTRUCTIONS you are
guaranteed to feel neat and tidy (but also a little short of breath)

5. If you don't follow THE INSTRUCTIONS

You will likely face some tricky moments. Apologies for this.
However, there is also a good chance that something

Strangeexcitingremarkableunexpectedslightlyfrighteningbut
brightlycoloured

will happen.

6. The choice

is yours.

Nick Toczek

Best-selling poet Nick Toczek writes every day and has published more than fifty books, some for adults, some for children.

He lives in Bradford in Yorkshire and is married to Gaynor. They have two grown-up children, two grandchildren, and a dog called Stan the Man.

As a writer-in-schools, Nick has visited thousands of UK schools as well as numerous overseas schools in almost fifty countries. He's also a professional magician, a skilled puppeteer, a journalist and radio presenter.

Seasick

'I don't feel whelk,' whaled the squid, sole-fully.
'What's up?' asked the doctopus.
'I've got sore mussels and a tunny-hake,' she told him.

'Lie down and I'll egg salmon you,' mermaid the doctopus.
'Rays your voice,' said the squid. 'I'm a bit hard of herring.'
'Sorry! I didn't do it on porpoise,' replied the doctopus orcwardly.

He helped her to oyster self on to his couch
And asked her to look up so he could sea urchin.
He soon flounder plaice that hurt.

'This'll make it eel,' he said, whiting a prescription.
'So I won't need to see the sturgeon?' she asked.
'Oh, no,' he told her. 'In a couple of dace you'll feel brill.'

'Cod bless you,' she said.
'That'll be sick squid,' replied the doctopus.

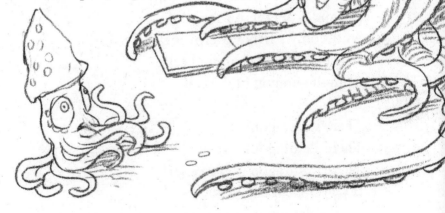

The Dragon in the Cellar

There's a dragon!
There's a dragon!
There's a dragon in the cellar!
Yeah, we've got a cellar-dweller.
There's a dragon in the cellar.

He's a cleanliness fanatic,
takes his trousers and his jacket
to the dragon in the attic
who puts powder by the packet
in a pre-set automatic
with a rattle and a racket
that's disturbing and dramatic.

There's a dragon!
There's a dragon!
There's a dragon in the cellar
with a flame that's red 'n' yeller.
There's a dragon in the cellar . . .

. . . and a dragon on the roof
who's only partly waterproof,
so she's borrowed an umbrella
from the dragon in the cellar.

There's a dragon!
There's a dragon!
There's a dragon in the cellar!
If you smell a panatella
it's the dragon in the cellar.

178

And the dragon from the study's
helping out his cellar buddy,
getting wet and soap-suddy
with the dragon from the loo
there to give a hand too,
while the dragon from the porch
supervises with a torch.
Though the dragon from the landing,
through a slight misunderstanding,
is busy paint-stripping and sanding.

There's a dragon!
There's a dragon!
There's a dragon in the cellar!
Find my dad, and tell the feller
there's a dragon in the cellar . . .

. . . where the dragon from my room
goes zoom, zoom, zoom
in a cloud of polish and spray-perfume,
cos he's the dragon whom
they pay to brighten up the gloom
with a mop and a duster and a broom, broom, broom.

There's a dragon!
There's a dragon!
There's a dragon in the cellar!
Gonna get my mum and tell her
there's a dragon in the cellar.

The Not-me Kid

The not-me kid
The not-me kid
Said that he didn't
But of course he did
So he became
The not-me kid.
That's his nickname:
The not-me kid.

'Not me! Not me!'
We heard him claim.
Oh, but it was.
He knew no shame.
He'd not confess.
We knew his game.
Getting off lightly
Was his aim.

The not-me kid
The not-me kid
Said that he didn't
But of course he did
So he became
The not-me kid.
That's his nickname:
The not-me kid.

'I'm innocent!'
He'd still proclaim,
Though 'Wasn't me!'
Now sounded tame
As every time
We'd get the same
String of excuses
Each one lame.

The not-me kid
The not-me kid
Said that he didn't
But of course he did
So he became
The not-me kid.
That's his nickname:
The not-me kid.

It's Festival Time!

A festival! A festival!
A friendly, family festival.
The time of year that's best of all.

A festival! A festival!
Forget all things detestable
And dance in clothes majestical.
Your worries are divestable.

A festival! A festival!
A friendly, family festival.
The time of year that's best of all.

A festival! A festival!
When food is most digestible,
And games are all contestable,
And presents are requestable.

A festival! A festival!
A friendly, family festival.
The time of year that's best of all.

A festival! A festival!
Sing songs and sound celestial.
Religions east and west have all
Got days they call a festival.

A festival! A festival!
A friendly, family festival.
The time of year that's best of all.
A festival! A festival!

Staff Meeting

The teachers have gathered in private to talk
About their collections of leftover chalk –
Bits that are rare, bits they just like,
And fragments they've saved just in case there's a strike.
One has a blue that you don't often see,
Another a remnant from nineteen-oh-three.

They've thousands of pieces in boxes and tins,
Each sorted and counted with tweezers and pins.
And when all their best bits have been on display,
They'll take them home carefully, and lock them away.

The End of School

We shove gloves and scarves on.
It's shivery and stark.
And out in the playground
It's evening and dark.
We rattle the railings
With sticks for a lark.

The sky's grown as grey
As the skin of a shark.
The branches are bare
On the trees in the park.
The wind took their leaves
Leaving winter-proof bark.

The streetlights are waking
And making their mark.
At first they're a dull red
And glow like a spark,
Grow orange, then yellow –
A dazzling arc.

'They're forecasting snow,'
I heard one mum remark.
Sleet comes, then the bus comes.
We loudly embark.
The sunshine of summer's
Fled south like the lark.

The Great Escape

In the Great Escape from London Zoo
eight caribou and gnu they knew
mounted a minor military coup,
an act of animal derring-do,
and locked the staff they overthrew
in the 'potamus pit and a portaloo,
then caught a plane to North Peru.

As animals broke out two-by-two
to squeal and growl and grunt and moo
a loud unruly queue soon grew
that wriggled and ran and crawled and flew,
stampeding down the avenue.

In the Great Escape from London Zoo
we heard how a herd of kangaroo
had bid the big brown owl adieu
with a: 'Toodle-oo, mate, toodle-oo!'
but before he'd time to twit-tu-woo
they'd hopped it, heading for Timbuktu
and the owl himself had flown off too.

While a crocodile and a cockatoo
crossed the Thames in a slim canoe,
rowed by the bird, so the croc could chew . . .
chew through the bones of the eight-man crew
till the river ran red instead of blue.

In the Great Escape from London Zoo
the pandas abandoned their bamboo
and, all dressed up as railway crew,
hijacked the fifteen fifty-two
from platform three of Waterloo
and 'parley-voo' they zoomed straight through
Paris, and on to Katmandu.

Panic ensued and ballyhoo
when pot-bellied pig and rare-breed ewe
gatecrashed a very posh barbecue
terribly upsetting the well-to-do
and causing a heck of a hullabaloo.

You doubt my word? What's wrong with you?
Why, every detail here is true.
The Great Escape from London Zoo
When was that? I thought you knew:
Years ago, at half-past two.

Pie Corbett

Pie Corbett writes poetry, stories and materials for teachers. He leads 'Talk for Writing' which takes him around the world, working with schools to improve literacy. He has been a columnist for the *Times Educational Supplement* as well as writing and editing over 250 books. His collection *Evidence of Dragons* is a classroom staple alongside editing 10 anthologies for Macmillan Children's Books.

He lives in the countryside with his family, who occasionally make guest appearances in his poems.

Praise Poem

Let us begin
    with the hottest of days
        and the shock of icy water sipped from frosted glass.

Let us begin
    with the tickle of a ladybird
        and the rosebud of its freckled red coat.

Let us begin
    with the fizz of sherbet lemon
        sizzling on the tongue.

Let us begin
    with the sudden grin and giggle
        of a joke cracked open like a walnut.

Let us begin
    with the cat's warm purr
        and the first crazy petals of snow falling.

Let us begin
    with the kicking of legs
        as the swing flings itself higher.

Let us begin
    with a blade of grass
        and sunlight pouring through clouds like golden dust.

Let us begin
    with the hot breath of chips on a cold night
        and the surprise of torchlight icing the dark.

Let us begin
    by counting the rings on your fingertips
        and the mystery of a magnet's pull.

Yes, let us begin
with such simple things.

The Playground Monster

It grabbed me
with its tarmac jaws
and then it tried
to bite me.

It grasped me
with its gravelly paws
and then it tried
to fight me.

I live in fear of walking
across its great black back.

I think it knows I'm talking.
It listens at a crack!

I fear its greedy darkness,
the way it seems to need

to reach out when I'm running
and grab me for a feed.

It grabbed me
with its tarmac jaws
and then it tried
to bite me.

It grasped me
with its gravelly paws
and then it tried
to fight me.

The Dragon Whistler

The Dragon Whistler
tucks stars into her pocket,
reaches far for a sunset;
purses her moonlit lips
and whistles . . .

she listens as
owls flutter,
hedgerows mutter
and the darkness scowls –

a dragon's eye blinks
as a chink of moonlight
slinks through the cave's grime.

Again and again
the whistle bristles
in the hot silence
of the dragon's brain.

The Dragon Whistler's call
drifts across carved valleys
and mountain peaks,
seeking the dragon's lair
where rusted swords rustle,
crusted crowns tussle
and the clink of coins chimes

as the dragons fly
and the Dragon Whistler
waits, still as the moon.
For soon, they will come.

Secret Poem

My secret is made of –
the fingertips of clouds,
the silence between heartbeats
found at a hospital bedside,
the hangman's gloves,
the stoat's bright eye,
the bullet as it slices
through the winter wind.

I found it –
on the edge of a lemon's bite,
clutched in the centre of a crocus,
held in a crisp packet,
crumpled at the side of the road
where the nettles stab
their sharp barbs
at the innocent child's hand.

This secret can –
prise open steel hearts,
smooth a stormy sea flat,
capture the wind,
cup the moon's shine
in an empty palm,
break apart Mount Everest
till it is powder
in a lover's pocket.

If I lost
this secret –
even the lonely mountain goat
would bleat . . .

A Chance in France

'Stay at home,'
Mum said,

But I
took a chance
in France,
turned grey
for the day
in St Tropez,

forgot what
I did
in Madrid,
had some tussles
in Brussels
with a trio
from Rio,
lost my way
in Bombay,
nothing wrong
in Hong Kong,
felt calmer
in Palma
and quite nice
in Nice,
yes, felt finer
in China,
took a room

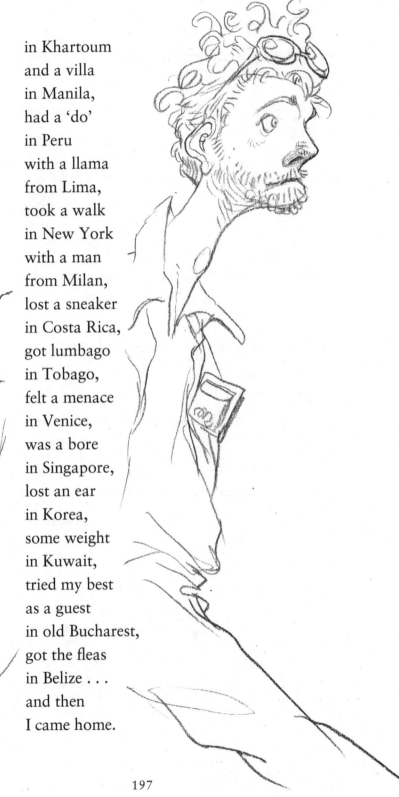

in Khartoum
and a villa
in Manila,
had a 'do'
in Peru
with a llama
from Lima,
took a walk
in New York
with a man
from Milan,
lost a sneaker
in Costa Rica,
got lumbago
in Tobago,
felt a menace
in Venice,
was a bore
in Singapore,
lost an ear
in Korea,
some weight
in Kuwait,
tried my best
as a guest
in old Bucharest,
got the fleas
in Belize . . .
and then
I came home.

The Inventor's Wife Speaks

'He was up late last night
inventing planets,

Sitting at his Workmate bench,
rolling stars between finger and thumb.

Then waiting
while they fired in the furnace to a thousand degrees.

He left them
on the windowsill to cool beneath moonlight.

Like tiny marbles
washed sea green, cloud softened and sky blue.

Tonight he'll be up late too –
it's always the same, the second night –

creatures to create,
planets to propagate –

he'll be crouched over his microscope,
tweezers in hand, hunched like eternity's question mark,

worrying in the dark,
soldiering fragments from his imagination

Why only last week
he showed me a butterfly elephant nimble as a bee

sipping nectar through its tiny trunk,
bumbling and stumbling, an aerodynamic impossibility.

Then when he's finished
he'll take to his bed, sleep deep and dream

more incredible and lovely planets,
many moons, stupendous suns and new skies.'

Winter Haiku

– 23 December 2003

Bitter dawn wind bites
     like a dog – clouds are sly cats
          slipping quietly by.

          Frozen puddles – leaves
               locked in ice, suspended in
                    a slice of cold time.

          Frosted grass catches
               sunlight – it glitters like
                    glass-splintered forests.

          Snow drifts across town
               in a swarm; a soft, white storm
                    kidnapping the streets.

          This morning the moon
               is a ghostly thumbprint traced
                    on shivers of blue.

          Winter dawn – the milk
               bottles are frosted; cars skid,
          cat-screech down the street.

Rachel Piercey

Rachel Piercey is a poet and editor who lives in London. Her poems for children have been widely published, including in *The Caterpillar*, comprehension textbooks from Bloomsbury and Schofield & Sims, and the Macmillan anthologies *She Will Soar*, *Poems for 8 Year Olds* and *We Wish You a Merry Christmas*.

Rachel is the founder and editor of *Tyger Tyger Magazine*, an online journal of new poems for children, which includes free poetry posters and teaching resources. She has also co-edited three children's poetry anthologies for The Emma Press on the subjects of mythology, space, and kings and queens. Rachel is a regular contributor to the Children's Poetry Summit blog, runs workshops in schools for The Poetry Society and teaches for The Poetry School.

Her search-and-find poetry-and-picture book, *If You Go Down to the Woods Today* has been translated into over twenty different languages. Rachel also writes for adults; her most recent pamphlet is *Disappointing Alice*, published by HappenStance in 2019.

This or That

So when does a kitten convert to a cat?
How many burst bubbles turn fizzy to flat?

How heavy is drizzle, before it's a shower?
Has anyone been there when bud becomes flower?

What point does a grape shrivel into a raisin?
What point does 'surprising' shift into 'amazing'?

What number of people turn 'some' into 'most'?
The thing that was far away, when is it close?

What stage do acquaintances deepen to friends?
A friendship might fizzle, but when does it end?

The moon's always changing and so, do you reckon,
she's full for no more than a pearlescent second?

And when are we coming and when are we going?
And when can our words be described as a poem?

If we're sure of our 'this' and we're sure of our 'that',
tell me when does a kitten convert to a cat?

On the Mat

The mat is six-of-us wide, and five-of-us long, and
    sprouting fur
in patches like a piglet I once patted. All the best
    things in class
happen here: story-time stillness, show and tell,
    and the five minutes
after break when there's a video glowing. Once a
    poet sat down here,
and I said the stars were like bright thoughts, and
    she put it in a poem.

ACROSTIC

A rather useful structure:
Cures the blank page straight away.
Requires creative juggling
Of what you want to say.
Some planning can be useful
To ensure that you include
Ideas to give the poem life, before you must
Conclude.

Fast Poem

Most of my poems are focused on slowing, although-ing,
    and knowing, and *why?*
But this poem here is a fast-flowing cheer to what goes in
    the flash of an eye.

I'll start with a rocket, a nothing-can-block-it, force
    socking it into the stars . . .
and proceed with a cheetah, a leap-out-and-eat-ya, the
    fleetest land-creature by far.

A peregrine's winging, a cricket ball's flinging, a marlin-fin
    parting the ocean;
an aeroplane, bullet train, A-to-B-back-again: brainy
    mechanical motion.

There's volt-footed Bolt, holding records for gold, halting
    others in ten seconds flat,
plus bolts sky-flung, and the Earth round the sun, and
    what's done at the drop of a hat.

Add rapid and intricate rhythms of rappers, add dominos
    flattened in lines,
and zipwire-flying, and new ideas firing, and suddenly
    changing your mind.

Then the speed of light, which is speed at its height, bright
    intergalactically glowing –
and lastly, most slow, but I gave it a go, this (frankly
    tongue-twistery) poem.

Bake Sale

Chocolatey cornflakes and coconut ice,
fruity Dundee cake and hot apple pies,
cool-bags of kulfi, Victoria sponge,
baklava, bundt cakes and fat currant buns,
lemony madeleines, light panettone,
treacly parkin and creamy cannoli,
beautiful mooncakes and apricot malva,
lamingtons, gingerbread, crumbling halva,
shattering chikki and rich bara brith,
brownies and buttery rugelach twists,
Black Forest gateau and candied cassata,
kipferl and strudel and fragrant gizzada,
checkerboard Battenberg, cobbler with peach:
I couldn't decide so I bought some of each.

School Orchestra

Rob plays recorder, both piercing and sweet.
Blake beats out time on the bass with his feet.
Vix bows her violin, pitched to the stars.
Finlay, on flute, blows a breeze through the bars.
Solomon's saxophone's story unfolds.
Charlie, on cello, tugs hard at our souls.
Xan rings the bones of the xylophone's spine.
Kaz, on the keyboard, finds depth in its shine.
Gita's guitar sounds like sunshine or rain.
Sab has the snap of the snare in her veins.
Sasha was put on this planet to sing.
And I crown it all with the triangle's *ting*.

Craft

We are making Viking longhouses
out of lollipop sticks and mine
won't fix together and the turf
has gone mangy and the door is
wonky and Amy's is so perfect
I smell woodsmoke and scorched iron,
I see a warrior with sea-salted hair
and a bright sword, who throws open
every door but mine and leads everyone
away over the silver-bladed ocean.

Kit Wright

Kit Wright was born in Kent and lives in East London. He likes writing poems for adults and children, walking in Epping Forest and singing songs to his guitar. People have been nice about his poems but are not always so kind about his singing. But he keeps singing.

Applause

I gave my cat a six-minute standing ovation
For services rendered: hunting of very small game,

Pouncing about and sitting in cardboard boxes,
Three-legged washing and never knowing his name,

The jump on the knee, the nuzzle at night, the kneading
Of dough with his paws, the punch at the candle flame,

The yowling for food, the looking at everything otherwise,
Staring through it straight with a faraway aim.

I gave my cat a six-minute standing ovation.
Your cat's like that? I think you should do the same.

The Magic Box

I will put in my box

the swish of a silk sari on a summer night,
fire from the nostrils of a Chinese dragon,
the hidden pass that steals through the mountains.

I will put in the box

a snowman with a rumbling belly,
a sip of the bluest water from Lake Lucerne,
a leaping spark from an electric fish.

I will put in the box

three violet wishes spoken in Gujarati,
the last joke of an ancient uncle
and the first smile of a baby.

I will put in the box

a fifth season and a black sun,
a cowboy on a broomstick
and a witch on a white horse.

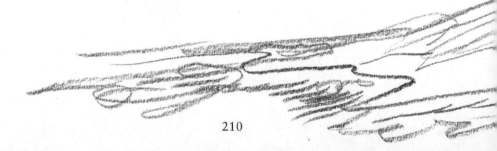

My box is fashioned from ice and gold and steel,
with stars on the lid and secrets in the corners.
Its hinges are the toe joints
of dinosaurs.

I shall surf on my box on the great
high-rolling breakers of the wild Atlantic,
then wash ashore on a yellow beach
the colour of the sun.

All of Us

All of us are afraid
More often than we tell.

There are times we cling like mussels to the sea-wall,
And pray that the pounding waves
Won't smash our shell.

Times we hear nothing but the sound
Of our loneliness, like a cracked bell
From fields far away where the trees are in icy shade.

O many a time in the night-time and in the day,
More often than we say,
We are afraid.

If people say they are never frightened,
I don't believe them.
If people say they are frightened,
I want to retrieve them

From that dark shivering haunt
Where they don't want to be,
Nor I.

Let's make of ourselves, therefore, an enormous sky
Over whatever
We most hold dear.

And we'll comfort each other,
Comfort each other's
Fear.

I Like You

When you're unkind
You don't mean to be.
And when you're kind
You couldn't care less
Whether or not
You're seen to be.

What I like about you
Is how you know what's cooking
In somebody else's mind.
You do the best you can
And you just don't care
Who's looking.

Rabbiting On

Where did you go?
Oh . . . nowhere much.

What did you see?
Oh . . . rabbits and such.

Rabbits? What else?
Oh . . . a rabbit hutch.

What sort of rabbits?
What sort? Oh . . . small.

What sort of hutch?
Just a hutch, that's all.

But what did it look like?
Like a rabbit hutch.

Well, what was in it?
Small rabbits and such.

I worried about you
While you were gone.

*Why don't you stop
Rabbiting on?*

The Thumb Bird*

The storm beats down
   And the thumb bird flies
High above the ocean
   Where the great whales go:

Tiniest of little ones
   That wing the skies,
Love light your journey
   When the wild winds blow . . .

And the thumb bird flies . . .
   And the thumb bird flies
     Far across the sea . . .

All among the pine trees
   She will make her nest
From moss and feathers
   In a cobweb sewn,

Till with her tiny ones
   She is blessed:
Love light their journey
   When they fly alone . . .

And the thumb bird flies . . .
And the thumb bird flies
Far across the sea . . .

Snuggled in the feathers
On the woodcock's back.
Taking a ride
On her way across the deep:

Though thunder roll
And lightning crack,
Love light your journey
Till you safely sleep . . .

And the thumb bird's flown . . .
And the thumb bird's flown
Far across the sea . . .

* *A name for the goldcrest, Britain's smallest bird.*

Red Boots On

Way down Geneva,
All along Vine,
Deeper than the snow drift
Love's eyes shine.

Mary Lou's walking
In the winter time.

She's got

Red boots on, she's got
Red boots on,
Kicking up the winter
Till the winter's gone.

So

Go by Ontario,
Look down Main,
If you can't find Mary Lou,
Come back again.

Sweet light burning
In winter's flame.

She's got

Snow in her eyes, got
A tingle in her toes
And new red boots on
Wherever she goes

So

All around Lake Street,
Up by St Paul,
Quicker than the white wind
Love takes all.

Mary Lou's walking
In the big snow fall.

She's got

Red boots on, she's got
Red boots on,
Kicking up the winter
Till the winter's gone.

Zaro Weil

Zaro Weil has been an actor, dancer, playwright, poet, historian, theatre director, educator and publisher. She co-founded a theatre dance company for children in Saint Louis, Missouri – Metro Theater Circus (now Metro Theater Company – MTC). For over ten years she wrote, directed, performed and taught in schools and universities throughout America, including several MTC guest stints at the John F Kennedy Center for the Performing Arts in Washington DC. She claims to have played every animal that ever existed, and some that didn't. Zaro's first widely praised collection of poems, *Mud, Moon and Me* was illustrated by Jo Riddell. Her collection *Cherry Moon* won the CLiPPA in 2020.

How to Get an Idea

Dig into mud
    or
Open up a new box of crayons
    or
Run your finger through a bag of marbles
    or
Skip a stone across water
    or
Ask a cat to lend you one
    or
Stand quietly under a dictionary
    or
Stick out your tongue and say, 'O!'
    or
Put an empty picture frame on the wall
    and wait

Shadows

moon
last evening you
rolled so loud and silver
past my window
that the shadows
woke and wove their dark
molasses stripes
over my bed
and
in the criss-cross of
that night-time
I knew what to do
breathe soft
breathe soft
and fold into a
quiet silhouette
until morning

A Parade of Beast Doodles

when I opened up today
and unwrapped the morning
I found a present

a sky full of clouds
all puff-pomps and shine-streaks
bubble-whites and lace-feathers
a canopy of stipple-shapes
a parade of beast-doodles and all
I could do was
lie down
to skybig
to clouddream
and wonder
what I might unwrap

this afternoon

Flicker and Flash

so many dragonflies

translucent whirligigs

each a tailspin
of flicker and flash
under this
perfumed peach sky

a thousand
tinselly rainbows
glance off wings
a million
miniature wind-curls
dance round them all

such capricious
summer sprites

cavorting forwards
hovering backwards

as though they have
all the time in the world
as though summer

will never end

Preposterous Penguins

thousands
of preposterously pensive penguins
pause to participate
in a particularly polar poetry pageant
probably in the perfectly pale and cold
penetrating South Pole

perhaps the precise problem is
every penguin parades around like
a posh peppy peacock
pretentiously presuming
to proclaim in a pesky pernickety way
they should (for pete's sake)
positively peep first

Hide and Seek

I decided to play a game with quiet

hide and seek
my turn
I slipped into the woods
looking for quiet
instead
a cacophony of forest-crackle
a hullabaloo of beast-babble
sprang towards me while
a Tweedledum of pandemonium
circled above
it was a free-for-all
and even the sun
jangled copper
between the leaves

so much for the forest

I went to the sea
searching for quiet
but the waves trumpeted
a rumbling ruckus
a crash of crinkle-crests while
squarking gulls sky-dived into
wind-trembled sea and
seashells crunched underfoot
as a medley of
fat green seaweed
slapped the sand
non-stop non-stop

so much for the sea

but then I turned
and quiet tagged me
I stopped
forest stopped
sea stopped
I found quiet
it must have been hiding
the whole time
inside my words
inside of me

HOWL

AIEEEEEEE AIEEEEEEE
OUEEEEEE OUEEEEE

OUOUOUOU OUOUOUOU

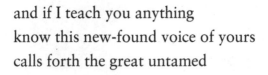

howl little cub
howl
don't hold back
flash those polished
amber eyes of yours
howl the scent of long ago

and if I teach you anything
know this new-found voice of yours
calls forth the great untamed

so when you want sun to rise
night to ignite its silent sparks
clear water to swell the river
howl

and when you stand
stiff-legged and tall
proud ears alert
teeth sharp-shined
confronting your prey
howl

of course when you must fly
escaping the bear
howl fierce
for earth rise up fast
to meet your lengthening legs

then howl soft
when first you meet your
grey-furred partner
under a moon-flood of trees
on a trail of sweet shadows

and howl long
when you smell that blue of
berries growing darkly wild
outside your very own den

last thing little cub
when your mother is no longer
hunting beside you
howl full
your big wolf heart
for me

AIEEEEEEE AIEEEEEEE
OUEEEEEE OUEEEEE
OUOUOUOU OUOUOUOU

Brian Patten

Brian Patten was born in Liverpool in 1946. His work first appeared in the bestselling Penguin collection *The Mersey Sound* in 1967 (with Roger McGough and the late Adrian Henri) which has now been reissued as a Penguin Modern Classic. Among his individual collections are *Little Johnny's Confession*, *Notes To The Hurrying Man*, *The Irrelevant Song*, *Vanishing Trick*, *Grave Gossip* and *Armada*. He is the editor of *The Puffin Book of Modern Children's Verse* and his poetry for children includes the highly popular collections *Gargling With Jelly*, *Thawing Frozen Frogs* and *Juggling With Gerbils*. He has won numerous awards, including The Cholmondeley Award for Poetry, and a special award from the Mystery Writers of America Guild for his children's novel, *Mr Moon's Last Case*. Brian has been honoured with the Freedom of the City of Liverpool and is a Fellow of the Royal Society of Literature, and of both Liverpool University and John Moores University as well as The Open University.

Rabbit's Spring

Snow
goes,

Ice
thaws,

Warm
paws!

Geography Lesson

Our teacher told us one day he would leave
And sail across a warm blue sea
To places he had only known from maps,
And all his life had longed to be.

The house he lived in was narrow and grey
But in his mind's eye he could see
Sweet-scented jasmine clinging to the walls,
And green leaves burning on an orange tree.

He spoke of the lands he longed to visit,
Where it was never drab or cold.
I couldn't understand why he never left,
And shook off the school's stranglehold.

Then halfway through his final term
He took ill and never returned.
He never got to that place on the map
Where the green leaves of the orange trees burned.

The maps were redrawn on the classroom wall;
His name forgotten, he faded away.
But a lesson he never knew he taught
Is with me to this day.

I travel to where the green leaves burn,
To where the ocean's glass-clear and blue,
To places our teacher taught me to love –
And which he never knew.

The Day I Got My Finger Stuck Up My Nose

When I got my finger stuck up my nose
I went to a doctor, who said,
'Nothing like this has happened before,
We will have to chop off your head.'

'It's only my finger stuck up my nose,
It's only my finger!' I said.
'I can see what it is,' the doctor replied,
'But we'll still have to chop off your head.'

He went to the cabinet. He took out an axe.
I watched with considerable dread.
'But it's only my finger stuck up my nose.
It's only a finger!' I said.

'Perhaps we can yank it out with a hook
Tied to some surgical thread.
Maybe we can try that,' he replied,
'Rather than chop off your head.'

'I'm never going to pick it again.
I've now learned my lesson,' I said.
'I won't stick my finger up my nose –
I'll stick it in my ear instead.'

Mr McGuire

Old Mr McGuire, blind as a bat,
had a rabbit, a weasel, a dog and a cat.
He stroked them all as he sat by the fire,
some days they felt smooth,
and some days like wire.
With a bark, a hiss, a squeak and miaow
they demanded attention
and all got it somehow.
Old Mr McGuire, he loved them all –
'To me you're one creature
you're all from the same sack.
God brought you here
and he'll take you back.
You may think you're different
but, heavens above –
you are all of you loved
with one single love.'

You Can't Be That

I told them:
When I grow up
I'm not going to be a scientist
Or someone who reads the news on TV.
No, a million bird will fly through me.
I'M GOING TO BE A TREE.

They said,
You can't be that. No, you can't be that.

I told them:
When I grow up
I'm not going to be an airline pilot,
A dancer, a lawyer or an MC.
No, huge whales will swim in me.
I'M GOING TO BE AN OCEAN!

They said,
You can't be that. No, you can't be that.

I told them:
I'm not going to be a DJ,
A computer programmer, a musician or beautician.
No, streams will flow through me, I'll be the home of eagles.
I'll be full of nooks, crannies, valleys and fountains.
I'M GOING TO BE A RANGE OF MOUNTAINS!

They said,
You can't be that. No, you can't be that.

I asked them:
Just what do you think I am?
Just a child, they said,
And children always become
At least one of the things
We want them to be.

They do not understand me.
I'll be a stable if I want, smelling of fresh hay,
I'll be a lost glade in which unicorns still play.
They do not realize I can fulfil any ambition.
They do not realize among them
Walks a magician.

Dear Mum,

While you were out
a cup went and broke itself,
a crack appeared in the blue vase
your great-great-grandad
brought back from Mr Ming in China.
Somehow, without me even turning on the tap,
the sink mysteriously overflowed.
A strange jam-stain,
about the size of a boy's hand,
appeared on the kitchen wall.
I don't think we will ever discover
exactly how the cat
managed to turn on the washing-machine
(especially from the inside),
or how Sis's pet rabbit went and mistook
the waste-disposal unit for a burrow.
I can tell you I was scared when,
as if by magic,
a series of muddy footprints
appeared on the new white carpet.
I was being good
(honest)
but I think the house is haunted so,
knowing you're going to have a fit,
I've gone over to Gran's for a bit.

A Small Dragon

I've found a small dragon in the woodshed.
Think it must have come from deep inside a forest
because it's damp and green and leaves
are still reflecting in its eyes.

I fed it on many things, tried grass,
the roots of stars, hazel-nut and dandelion,
but it stared up at me as if to say, I need
foods you can't provide.

It made a nest among the coal,
not unlike a bird's but larger,
it is out of place here
and is quite silent.

If you believed in it I would come
hurrying to your house to let you share my wonder,
but I want instead to see
if you yourself will pass this way.

Julia Donaldson

Julia Donaldson has written some of the world's best-loved children's books, including modern classics *The Gruffalo* and *The Gruffalo's Child*, which together have sold over 25 million copies worldwide and have been translated into over one hundred languages. Her other books include *Room on the Broom*, *Stick Man* and *Zog*, illustrated by Axel Scheffler, *The Hospital Dog*, illustrated by Sara Ogilvie and the hugely successful *What the Ladybird Heard* adventures, illustrated by Lydia Monks. Julia also writes fiction, including the Princess Mirror-Belle series, illustrated by Lydia Monks, as well as poems, plays and songs – and her brilliant live shows are always in demand. She was the UK Children's Laureate 2011–13 and has been honoured with a CBE for Services to Literature. Julia and her husband Malcolm divide their time between West Sussex and Edinburgh.

I Opened a Book

I opened a book and in I strode.
Now nobody can find me.
I've left my chair, my house, my road,
My town and my world behind me.

I'm wearing the cloak, I've slipped on the ring,
I've swallowed the magic potion.
I've fought with a dragon, dined with a king
And dived in a bottomless ocean.

I opened a book and made some friends.
I shared their tears and laughter
And followed their road with its bumps and bends
To the happily ever after.

I finished my book and out I came.
The cloak can no longer hide me.
My chair and my house are just the same,
But I have a book inside me.

There Go the Feet

Horses' hoofs on the cobbles clatter.
Pigeon toes on the pavement patter.
Clatter, patter,
There go the feet.

High-heeled shoes on the floorboards tap.
Divers' flippers on the wet sand flap.
Tap, flap,
Clatter, patter,
There go the feet.

Bedroom slippers on the staircase shuffle.
Football boots on the playing field scuffle.
Shuffle, scuffle,
Tap, flap,
Clatter, patter,
There go the feet.

Ballet pumps on the dance floor trip.
Woolly socks on the lino slip.
Trip, slip,
Shuffle, scuffle,
Tap, flap,
Clatter, patter,
There go the feet.

Rabbits' claws in the burrow scrabble.
Children's toes in the water dabble.
Scrabble, dabble,
Trip, slip,
Shuffle, scuffle,
Tap, flap,
Clatter, patter,
There go the feet.

Elephants' feet in the jungle crash.
Wellington boots in the puddles splash.
Crash, splash,
Scrabble, dabble,
Trip, slip,
Shuffle, scuffle,
Tap, flap,
Clatter, patter,
There go the feet.

Size-one shoes in the playpen toddle.
Ducklings' feet round the duck pond waddle.
Toddle, waddle,
Crash, splash,
Scrabble, dabble,
Trip, slip,
Shuffle, scuffle,
Tap, flap,
Clatter, patter,
THERE GO THE FEET!

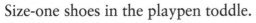
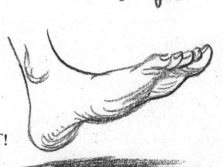

Come to the Library

Everyone is welcome to walk through the door.
It really doesn't matter if you're rich or poor.
There are books in boxes and books on shelves.
They're free for you to borrow, so help yourselves.

Come and meet your heroes, old and new,
From William the Conqueror to Winnie the Pooh.
You can look into the *Mirror* or read *The Times*,
Or bring along a toddler to chant some rhymes.

The librarian's a friend who loves to lend,
So see if there's a book that she can recommend.
Read that book, and if you're bitten
You can borrow all the other ones the author's written.

Are you into battles or biography?
Are you keen on gerbils or geography?
Gardening or ghosts? Sharks or science fiction?
There's something here for everyone, whatever your addiction.

There are students revising, deep in concentration,
And school kids doing projects, finding inspiration.
Over in the corner there's a table with seating,
So come along and join in the Book Club meeting.

Yes, come to the library! Browse and borrow,
And help make sure it'll still be here tomorrow.

Noisy Garden

If tiger lilies and dandelions growled,
And cowslips mooed, and dog roses howled,
And snapdragons roared and catmint miaowed,
My garden would be extremely loud.

The Mouse and the Lion

In the hottest sun of the longest day
A lion lay down for a doze.
A little brown mouse pattered out to play.
He danced on the whiskery nose.
Pit-a-pat, pit-a-pat, pit-a-pat, pit-a-pat,
He danced on the whiskery nose.

The lion awoke with a sneeze, 'A-choo!'
He picked up the mouse in his paw.
'And who may I venture to ask are you?'
He said with a terrible roar.
Grr, grrr, grrrrr, GRRRRRR,
He said with a terrible roar.

'I'll save your life if you'll let me go.'
The mouse's voice shook as he spoke.
The lion laughed loudly, 'Oh ho ho ho.
I'll let you go free for your joke.'
Oho, oho, ohohohoho,
I'll let you go free for your joke.

As chance would have it, the following week
The lion was caught in a net
When all of a sudden he heard a squeak:
'Well met, noble lion, well met.'
Squeak, squeak, squeak, squeak,
Well met, noble lion, well met.

The little mouse nibbled and gnawed and bit
Till the lion was finally free.
'It's nothing, dear lion, don't mention it:
I'm repaying your kindness to me.'
Nibbly, nibbly, nibbly, nibble,
Repaying your kindness to me.

'For one of the lessons which mice must learn
From their whiskery father and mother
Is the famous old saying that one good turn
Always deserves another.'
Pit-a-pat, grrr, ohoho, squeak!
Always deserves another.

Shuffle and Squelch

Spring brings showers; the world's aflood.
Wellies on, let's brave the mud.
We'll go squelching about, squelching about,
Squelching about in the mud,
Yes we'll go squelching about, squelching about,
Squelching about in the mud.

Kick your boots off, everyone.
Summer's here and so's the sun.
We'll go dancing about, dancing about,
Dancing about in the sun,
Yes we'll go dancing about, dancing about,
Dancing about in the sun.

Hold your hat; the winds are thieves.
Watch them steal the autumn leaves
As we shuffle about, shuffle about,
Shuffle about in the leaves,
Yes as we shuffle about, shuffle about,
Shuffle about in the leaves.

Wind your scarf round once or twice.
Winter's turned the world to ice.
We'll go sliding about, sliding about,
Sliding about on the ice,
Yes we'll go sliding about, sliding about,
Sliding about on the ice.

Santa Claws

I don't know why they're blaming me
When all I did was climb a tree
And bat a shiny silver ball.
How could I know the tree would fall?
And when those silly lights went out
They didn't have to scream and shout
And turf me out and shut the door.
Now no one loves me any more.
I'm in the kitchen by myself.
But wait! What's on that high-up shelf?
A lovely turkey, big and fat!
How nice! They *do* still love their cat.

Jenny Joseph

Jenny Joseph was one of Britain's best-loved poets, and the author of numerous poetry collections, books for children and volumes of prose. She was born in Birmingham in 1932, but her first remembered home was in leafy Buckinghamshire on the edge of the Chilterns not far from the Thames. Other important childhood places were Dorset (she learned to ride a bicycle the winter Poole Harbour froze over) and, later, the North Devon coast. Books were always important to her. She left school when she was fifteen and went abroad to learn languages. Later she got a scholarship to study English at St Hilda's College, Oxford. Jenny did a variety of jobs, from cleaning to teaching to being a pub landlady.

Her most famous poem is 'Warning', written in 1961 and twice voted Britain's favourite poem of the twentieth century. It has been reproduced throughout the world and translated into many languages. Jenny was made a Fellow of the Royal Society of Literature in 1999.

Having Visitors

I heard you were coming and
Thrum thrum thrum
Went something in my heart like a
Drum drum drum.

I briskly walked down the
Street street street
To buy lovely food for us to
Eat eat eat.

I cleaned the house and filled it with
Flowers flowers flowers
And asked the sun to drink up the
Showers showers showers.

Steadily purring
Thrum, thrum, thrum
Went the drum in my heart because
You'd come, come, come.

The Magic of the Brain

Such a sight I saw:
An eight-sided kite surging up into a cloud
Its eight tails streaming out as if they were one.
It lifted my heart as starlight lifts the head
Such a sight I saw.

And such a sound I heard:
One bird through dim winter light as the day was closing
Poured out a song suddenly from an empty tree.
It cleared my head as water refreshes the skin
Such a sound I heard.

Such a smell I smelled:
A mixture of roses and coffee, of green leaf and warmth.
It took me to gardens and summer and cities abroad,
Memories of meetings as if my past friends were here
Such a smell I smelled.

Such soft fur I felt:
It wrapped me around, soothing my winter-cracked skin,
Not gritty or stringy or sweaty but silkily warm
As my animal slept on my lap, and we both breathed content
Such soft fur I felt.

Such food I tasted:
Smooth-on-tongue soup, and juicy crackling of meat,
Greens like fresh fields, sweet-on-your-palate peas,
Jellies and puddings and fragrance of fruit they are made from
Such good food I tasted.

Such a world comes in:
Far world of the sky to breathe in through your nose
Near world you feel underfoot as you walk on the land.
Through your eyes and your ears and your mouth and your
 brilliant brain
Such a world comes in.

The Things I See

Hurry hurry hurry
It won't do you no good though.
The lights ahead are red
You go up to them slap bang
Rocking on your chassis.
Meanwhile you have missed
What I have seen –
A small boy hiding behind a tree
And the buds breaking out all around him, kissed
With little tongues of green.

Angry angry angry.
It won't do you no good though
For the catch on the door will slide
When you push your boxes through at that hasty angle.
The red fuming skin of your face
Must be all your eyes can see.
Meanwhile you have missed
What I have seen –
A woman with a strange patched face
Looking up into the spring sky through the mist
In her light eyes for Heaven's Queen.

Furry furry furry
It won't do you much good though
To be wrapped so warm to the eyes
That you cannot turn your head
That you miss what I have seen –
All the things I see:
A tall man like a pole
And at the bottom of his long arms, down at his feet
A tiny little pushchair and a tiny baby
Sunk in its hammocky seat between the wheels;
A little girl sitting high up on her father's arm
With a long furry tail laid heavy among her ringlets
Swinging from her Davy Crockett hat;
And two extraordinary pigeons
Of quite different and glistening colours.
And a cloak of St Francis brown and a Mary's blue
Walking together, collecting the dust of the street
All the things that I see
As I hurry hurry hurry
To work, but slowly, slowly.

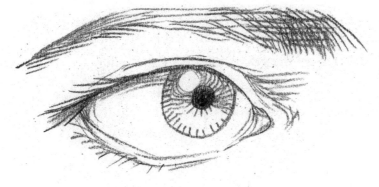

The Life of Feet

Walking, walking down by the sea
Walking, walking up on the hill
Strong feet, long feet
Squat feet, young feet
Making tracks on paths
Shuffling through the leaves
Going with a purpose

Feeling the sand and the waves
Knowing the grass and the land.

Running, running in through the gate
Clattering, jumping, up to the steps
Shapely feet, firm feet
Straight feet, tired feet
Coming home after play
Up the steps to the door
Glad to have a rest

Warmed by the sand, soothed by the waves
Cooled by the grass, firmed by the land

Good strong walking feet.

Warning

When I am an old woman I shall wear purple
With a red hat which doesn't go, and doesn't suit me.
And I shall spend my pension on brandy and summer gloves
And satin sandals, and say we've no money for butter.
I shall sit down on the pavement when I'm tired
And gobble up samples in shops and press alarm bells
And run my stick along the public railings
And make up for the sobriety of my youth.
I shall go out in my slippers in the rain
And pick flowers in other people's gardens
And learn to spit.

You can wear terrible shirts and grow more fat
And eat three pounds of sausages at a go
Or only bread and pickle for a week
And hoard pens and pencils and beermats and things in boxes.

But now we must have clothes that keep us dry
And pay our rent and not swear in the street
And set a good example for the children.
We must have friends to dinner and read the papers.

But maybe I ought to practise a little now?
So people who know me are not too shocked and surprised
When suddenly I am old, and start to wear purple.

Another Story of Red Riding Hood

I know a girl who's fit to eat
I know a girl with good strong feet
For walking;
I know a girl with sparkly eyes
I know a girl who doesn't tell lies,
My darling.

I know a wolf in a forest lair
Plotting and planning with great care
For dinner
To trick a girl who's thoughtful and kind.
It's always in her Grandma's mind
To win her

Away from the dangers of the wood
And keep her safe if only she could
Protect her.
The wolf is slinking through the trees
And he must hurry if he's
To collect her.

The girl, too sensible to stay
And dilly-dally on the way,
Was singing.
Her bag held her and Granny's luncheon
From it her father's hawthorn truncheon
Was swinging.

This was the song that she sang to the wolf
To the hungry wolf who grumbled and snarled:

You are bad and I am good
You stay in your part of the wood,
I'll keep my way.
You can have my sandwiches for lunch
(They're juicier than Gran's bones to munch).
Then go away.

She shouted and waved her stick and danced
And the wolf saw a pigeon, as it chanced,
Deep in the wood.
Thinking as always about her Gran
Like a mile-a-minute sprinter ran
Red Riding Hood.

Getting Back Home

Hang your hat on the peg
Rest up, rest up
Fling your coat on the bed
For you have travelled many miles to see me.

Put your feet on the bench
Rest up, rest up
Heave off your heavy boots
For you have come through winter days to see me.

Settle down by the fire
Rest up, rest up
Lean back and smile at me
For after all this time and travelling
Oh traveller, I'm glad to see you.

James Berry

James was born in a north-east coastal village in Portland, Jamaica, West Indies. He went to work on farms in the USA in the 1940s and then came to live in England in 1948.

He started developing his writing while he worked as an international telegraphist for British Telecom. He was the author of a number of poetry collections for children and adults and he won the Signal Poetry Award for his collection *When I Dance* in 1989. His selected poems for children *Only One of Me* has recently been published.

When I Dance

When I dance it isn't merely
That music absorbs my shyness,
My laughter settles in my eyes,
My swings of arms convert my frills
As timing tunes my feet with floor
As if I never just looked on.

It is that when I dance
O music expands my hearing
And it wants no mathematics,
It wants no thinking, no speaking,
It only wants all my feeling
In with animation of place.

When I dance it isn't merely
That surprises dictate movements,
Other rhythms move my rhythms,
I uncradle rocking-memory
And skipping, hopping and running
All mix movements I balance in.

It is that when I dance
I'm costumed in a rainbow mood,
I'm okay at any angle,
Outfit of drums crowds madness round,
Talking winds and plucked strings conspire,
Beat after beat warms me like sun.

When I dance it isn't merely
I shift bodyweight balances
As movement amasses my show,
I celebrate each dancer here,
No sleep invades me now at all
And I see how I am tireless.

It is that when I dance
I gather up all my senses
Well into hearing and feeling,
With body's flexible postures
Telling their poetry in movement
And I celebrate all rhythms.

One

Only one of me
and nobody can get a second one
from a photocopy machine.

Nobody has the fingerprints I have.
Nobody can cry my tears, or laugh my laugh
or have my expectancy when I wait.

But anybody can mimic my dance with my dog.
Anybody can howl how I sing out of tune.
And mirrors can show me multiplied
many times, say, dressed up in red
or dressed up in grey.

Nobody can get into my clothes for me
or feel my fall for me, or do my running.
Nobody hears my music for me, either.

I am just this one.
Nobody else makes the words
I shape with sound, when I talk.

But anybody can act how I stutter in a rage.
Anybody can copy echoes I make.
And mirrors can show me multiplied
many times, say, dressed up in green
or dressed up in blue.

Playing a Dazzler

You bash drums playing a dazzler;
I worry a trumpet swaying with it.

You dance, you make a girl's skirt swirl;
I dance, I dance by myself.

You bowl, I lash air and my wicket;
I bowl, you wallop boundary balls.

Your goal-kick beat me between my knees;
my goal kick flies into a pram-and-baby.

You eat off your whole-pound chocolate cake;
I swell up halfway to get my mate's help.

My bike hurls me into the hedge;
your bike swerves half-circle from trouble.

I jump the wall and get dumped;
you leap over the wall and laugh, satisfied.

I touch the country bridge and walk;
you talk and talk.

You write poems with line-end rhymes;
I write poems with rhymes nowhere or anywhere.

Your computer game screens monsters and gunners;
my game brings on swimmers and courting red birds.

Postcard Poem: Solo

Mum, you needn't have worried one bit.
I travelled fine, fine, solo. Carried
in steelbird-belly of music shows.
I ate two passengers' pudding twice.
Nibbled nothings nutty and chocolatey.
Sipped cool Cokes. Had more nibbles.
All over mountain after mountain.
Over different oceans. Over
weird clouds, like snow hills
with trails of straggly shapes
drifting, searching. And strangers
talked – Germans going on big-fish hunt,
Italians to ride glass-bottomed boat,
a Dane to do snorkelling. Then, Mum,
I hopped from steelbird-belly, down among
sun-roasted people of a palmtree place.
Welcome to Jamaica, voices called out.
While family hugged a sweating me
and took me off. Other exotics
got collected up in cars and coaches
to be naked on beaches, while
steelbird stood there shiny-ready
for more come-and-go trips.

A Nest Full of Stars

Only chance made me come and find
my hen, stepping from her hidden
nest, in our kitchen garden.

In her clever secret place, her tenth
egg, still warm, had just been dropped.

Not sure of what to do, I picked up
every egg, counting them, then put them
down again. *All were mine.*

All swept me away and back.
I blinked. I saw: a whole hand
of ripe bananas, nesting.

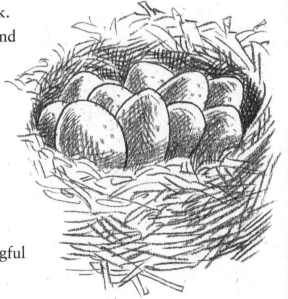

I blinked, I saw: a basketful
of ripe oranges, nesting.

I blinked, I saw: a trayful
of ripe naseberries, nesting.

I blinked, I saw: an open bagful
of ripe mangoes, nesting.

I blinked, I saw:
a mighty nest full of stars.

Isn't My Name Magical?

Nobody can see my name on me.
My name is inside
and all over me, unseen
like other people also keep it.
Isn't my name magical?

My name is mine only.
It tells I am individual,
the one special person it shakes
when I'm wanted.

Even if someone else answers
for me, my message hangs in air
haunting others, till it stops
with me, the right name.
Isn't your name and my name magic?

If I'm with hundreds of people
and my name gets called,
my sound switches me on to answer
like it was my human electricity.

My name echoes across playground,
It comes, it demands my attention.
I have to find out who calls,
who wants me for what.
My name gets blurted out in class,
it is terror, at a bad time,
because somebody is cross.

My name gets called in a whisper
I am happy, because
My name may have touched me
with a loving voice.
Isn't your name and my name magic?

Okay, Brown Girl, Okay

For Josie, nine years old, who wrote to me saying, 'Boys called me names because of my colour. I felt very upset . . . my brother and sister are English. I wish I was, then I won't be picked on . . . How do you like being brown?'

Josie, Josie, I am okay
being brown. I remember,
every day dusk and dawn get born
from the loving of night and light
who work together, like married.
    And they would like to say to you:
    Be at school on and on, brown Josie
    like thousands and thousands and thousands
    of children, who are brown and white
    and black and pale-lemon colour.
    All the time, brown girl Josie is okay.

Josie, Josie, I am okay
being brown. I remember,
every minute sun in the sky
and ground of the earth work together
like married.
  And they would like to say to you:
  Ride on up a going escalator
  like thousands and thousands and thousands
  of people, who are brown and white
  and black and pale-lemon colour.
  All the time, brown girl Josie is okay.

Josie, Josie, I am okay
being brown. I remember,
all the time bright-sky and brown-earth
work together, like married
making forests and food and flowers and rain.
  And they would like to say to you:
  Grow and grow brightly, brown girl.
  Write and read and play and work.
  Ride bus or train or boat or aeroplane
  like thousands and thousands and thousands
  of people, who are brown and white
  and black and pale-lemon colour.
  All the time, brown girl Josie is okay.

Carol Ann Duffy

Carol Ann Duffy lives in Manchester, where she is Professor and Creative Director of the Writing School at Manchester Metropolitan University. Her poetry has received many awards, including the Signal Prize for Children's Verse. She was Poet Laureate of the United Kingdom from 2009 to 2019.

Teacher

When you teach me,
your hands bless the air
where chalk dust sparkles.

And when you talk,
the six wives of Henry VIII
stand in the room like bridesmaids,

or the Nile drifts past the classroom window,
the Pyramids baking like giant cakes
on the playing fields.

You teach with your voice,
so a tiger prowls from a poem
and pads between desks, black and gold

in the shadow and sunlight,
or the golden apples of the sun drop
from a branch in my mind's eye.

I bow my head again
to this tattered, doodled book
and learn what love is.

The Oldest Girl in the World

Children, I remember how I could hear
with my soft young ears
the tiny sounds of the air –
tinkles and chimes
like minuscule bells
ringing continually there;
clinks and chinks
like glasses of sparky gooseberry wine,
jolly and glinting and raised in the air.
Yes, I could hear like a bat. And how!
Can't hear a sniff of it now.

Truly, believe me, I could all the time see
every insect that crawled in a bush,
every bird that hid in a tree,
individually.
If I wanted to catch a caterpillar
to keep as a pet in a box
I had only to watch a cabbage
and there it would be,
crawling bendy and green towards me.
Yes, I could see with the eyes of a cat. Miaow!
Can't see a sniff of it now.

And my sense of taste was second to none.
By God, the amount I knew with my tongue!
The shrewd taste of a walnut's brain.

The taste of a train from a bridge.
Of a kiss. Of air chewy with midge.
Of fudge from a factory two miles away
from the house where I lived.
I'd stick out my tongue
to savour the sky in a droplet of rain.
Yes, I could taste like the fang of a snake! Wow!
Can't taste a sniff of it now.

On the scent, what couldn't I smell
with my delicate nose, my nostrils of pearl?
I could smell the world!
Snow. Soot. Soil.
Satsumas in their Christmas sock.
The ink of a pen.
The stink of an elephant's skin.
The blue broth of a swimming pool. Dive in!
The showbizzy gasp of the wind.
Yes, I could smell like a copper's dog. Bow-wow!
Can't smell a sniff of it now.

As for my sense of touch
it was too much!
The cold of a snowball
felt through the vanishing heat of a mitt.
A peach like an apple wearing a vest.
The raffia dish of a bird's nest
A hot chestnut
branding the palm at the heart of the fist.

The stab of the thorn on the rose. Long grass, its itch.
Yes, I could feel with the sensitive hand of a ghost.
  Whooo!
Can't feel a sniff of it now.

Can't see a
Can't hear a
Can't taste a
Can't smell a
Can't feel a bit of it whiff of it niff of it.
Can't get a sniff of it now.

Sharp Freckles

For Ben Simmons

He picks me up, his big thumbs under my armpits tickle,
then puts me down. On his belt there is a shining silver buckle.
I hold his hand and see, close up, the dark hairs on his knuckles.

He sings to me. His voice is loud and funny and I giggle.
Now we will eat. I listen to my breakfast as it crackles.
He nods and smiles. His eyes are birds in little nests of wrinkles.

We kick a ball, red and white, between us. When he tackles
I'm on the ground, breathing a world of grass. It prickles.
He bends. He lifts me high above his head. Frightened, I wriggle.

Face to face, I watch the sweat above each caterpillar-
　　eyebrow trickle.
He rubs his nose on mine, once, twice, three times,
　　and we both chuckle.
He hasn't shaved today.
　　He kisses me.
　　He has sharp freckles.

A Week as My Home Town

Monday:
Rain. I'm the Library, round-shouldered, my stone brow
frowning at pigeons, my windows steamed up
like spectacles, my swing doors tut-tutting, my bricks
beginning to feel the damp.
                              Readers come,
whispering and coughing, shaking umbrellas
at the back of my yawning marble throat. My old lifts sigh
up and down, up and down, up and down. *Sssssshhh.*

Books flap in my head like birds.

Tuesday:
Weak sun. I'm the Park. My trees
wear last night's rain like jewels.
I shake birds from my hair as I wake, gargle
with a water-fountain, admire my green face
in the mirror of a small lake.
                              My thoughts
are a game of bowls, slow and calm.
I hum to myself in a lawnmower bass
among my bright municipal flowers,
my namesake benches.

Wednesday:
Fog. Museum, me. I hark back
to the past for endless hours, hoard
bronze coins in glass wallets, keep
long-gone summer butterflies on pins.

I remember things, pick
over old bones, look under cold stones,
check the names of the Kings and Queens
who sat on the gold thrones.

My stained-glass eyes stare inwards.

Thursday:
Sunshine. I'm the Main Road.
I lie on my back, stretch out
my side-street arms, wriggle
my alley toes, my mews fingers.

My throat is a tunnel
under a river. I burp cars
into the sparkling daylight,
belch lorries and juggernauts.

My heart's a roundabout,
in love with the next town.

Friday:
Grey cloud. I'm the Cinema, daydream
all day, can't sleep at night, hear

voices . . . *to infinity and beyond* . . . see
faces . . . *I'm all aloooone* . . . smell

popcorn . . . *please sir, can I have
some more* . . . They shine a light

in my eyes, prod at my plush red teeth.
I want to phone home. I'll be right here.

Saturday:
Frost. I'm the Disco. My neon lips
pout at the shivery night. My heart thumps
so loud the queue outside can hear it.

I wear light, glitterballs, lasers, strobe,
too much perfume. One day I'll give up smoking.
If anyone asks if I'm dancing, I'm dancing.

Sunday:
Snow. I'm the Church,
stone-flags for my shoes,
for my hat a steeple.

I kneel by the side of the graves
and sob with my bells.
Where are the people?

Meeting Midnight

I met Midnight.
Her eyes were sparkling pavements after frost.
She wore a full-length, dark blue raincoat with a hood.
She winked. She smoked a small cheroot.

I followed her.
Her walk was more a shuffle, more a dance.
She took the path to the river, down she went.
On Midnight's scent,
I heard the twelve cool syllables, her name,
chime from the town.
When those bells stopped,

Midnight paused by the water's edge.
She waited there.
I saw a girl in purple on the bridge.
It was One O'Clock.
Hurry, Midnight said, *it's late, it's late*.
I saw them run together.
Midnight wept.
They kissed full on the lips
and then I slept.

The next day I bumped into Half-Past Four.
He was a bore.

The Giantess

Where can I find seven small girls to be pets,
where can I find them?
One to comb the long grass of my hair
with this golden rake,
one to dig with this copper spade
the dirt from under my nails.
I will pay them in crab-apples.

Where can I find seven small girls to help me,
where can I find them?
A third to scrub at my tombstone teeth
with this mop in its bronze bucket,
a fourth to scoop out the wax from my ears
with this platinum trowel.
I will pay them in yellow pears.

Where can I find seven small girls to be good dears,
where can I find them?
A fifth one to clip the nails of my toes
with these sharp silver shears,
a sixth to blow my enormous nose
with this satin sheet.
I will pay them in plums.

But the seventh girl will stand on the palm of my hand,
singing and dancing,
and I will love the tiny music of her voice,
her sweet little jigs.
I will pay her in grapes and kumquats and figs.
Where can I find her?
Where can I find seven small girls to be pets?

Dimples

When I'm scared the Monsters are thrilling me.
When I'm cold the North Wind is chilling me.
When I'm pretty some ribbons are frilling me.
When I'm fibbing my teacher is grilling me.
When I'm sad my salt tears are spilling free.
When I'm brave my courage is willing me.
When I'm fidget my Grandma is stilling me.
When I'm hungry my Mother is filling me.
When I'm spending the toy shop is billing me.
When I score the referee's nilling me.
When I'm ill the doctor is pilling me.
When it's dawn the sparrows are trilling me.
But when I laugh and laugh and laugh and laugh
and laugh MY DIMPLES ARE KILLING ME!

Gareth Owen

Gareth Owen was born in Ainsdale, Lancashire. At school, his only ambition was to play mid-field for Everton and England. He tried many different jobs before he was accepted for a teacher training course at Bretton Hall College of Education near Wakefield. It changed his life. He found he had something of a talent for writing and acting. While teaching, he began writing poems for the children in his class and has now published some six collections. In addition to the prize-winning poetry, he has also written novels and plays, three of which have been broadcast by the BBC.

Den to Let

To let
One self-contained
Detached den.
Accommodation is compact
Measuring one yard square.
Ideal for two eight-year-olds
Plus one small dog
Or two cats
Or six gerbils.
Accommodation consists of:
One living room
Which doubles as kitchen
Bedroom
Entrance-hall
Dining room
Dungeon
Space capsule
Pirate boat
Covered wagon
Racing car
Palace
Aeroplane
Junk-room
And lookout post.
Property is southward facing
And can be found
Within a short walking distance

Of the back door
At bottom of garden.
Easily found in the dark
By following the smell
Of old cabbages and tea bags
Convenient escape routes
Past rubbish dump
To Seager's Lane
Through hole in hedge,
Or into next door's garden;
But beware of next door's rhinoceros
Who sometimes thinks he's a poodle.
Construction is of
Sound corrugated iron
And roof doubles as shower
During rainy weather.
Being partially underground,
Den makes
A particularly effective hiding place
When in a state of war
With older sisters
Brothers
Angry neighbours
Or when you simply want to be alone.
Some repair work needed
To north wall
Where Mr Spence's foot came through
When planting turnips last Thursday.
With den go all contents

Including:
One carpet – very smelly
One teapot – cracked
One woolly penguin –
No beak and only one wing
One unopened tin
Of sultana pud
One hundred and three *Beanos*
Dated 1983–1985
And four *Rupert* annuals.
Rent is free
The only payment being
That the new occupant
Should care for the den
In the manner to which it has been accustomed
And on long summer evenings
Heroic songs of days gone by
Should be loudly sung
So that old and glorious days
Will never be forgotten.

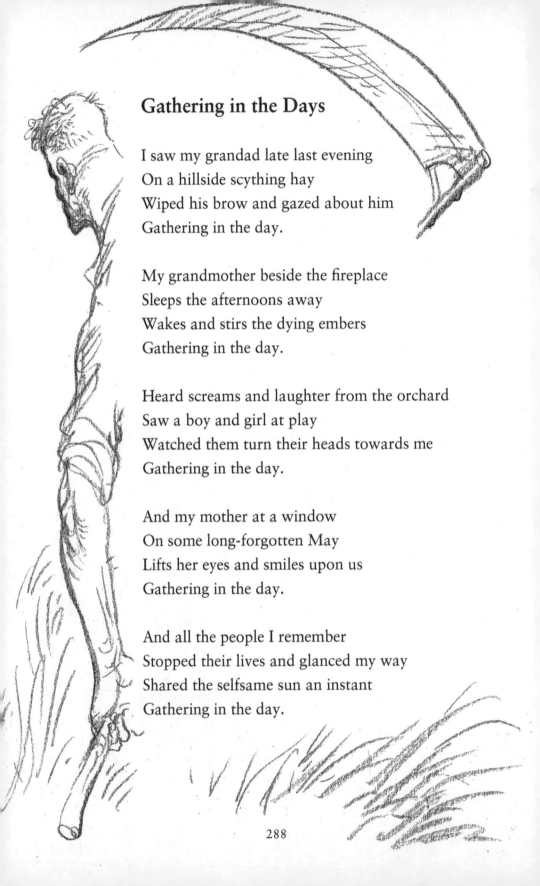

Gathering in the Days

I saw my grandad late last evening
On a hillside scything hay
Wiped his brow and gazed about him
Gathering in the day.

My grandmother beside the fireplace
Sleeps the afternoons away
Wakes and stirs the dying embers
Gathering in the day.

Heard screams and laughter from the orchard
Saw a boy and girl at play
Watched them turn their heads towards me
Gathering in the day.

And my mother at a window
On some long-forgotten May
Lifts her eyes and smiles upon us
Gathering in the day.

And all the people I remember
Stopped their lives and glanced my way
Shared the selfsame sun an instant
Gathering in the day.

Miss Creedle Teaches Creative Writing

'This morning,' cries Miss Creedle,
'We're all going to use our imaginations,
We're going to close our eyes 3W and imagine.
Are we ready to imagine, Darren?
I'm going to count to three.
At one, we wipe our brains completely clean;
At two, we close our eyes;
And at three, we imagine.
Are we all imagining? Good.
Here is a piece of music by Beethoven to help us.
Beethoven's dates were 1770 to 1827.
(See The Age of Revolutions in your History books.)
Although Beethoven was deaf and a German
He wrote many wonderful symphonies,
But this was a long time before anyone of us was born.
Are you imagining a time before you were born?
What does it look like? Is it dark?
(Embryo is a good word you might use.)
Does the music carry you away like a river?
What is the name of the river? Can you smell it?
Foetid is an exciting adjective.
As you float down the river
Perhaps you land on an alien planet.
Tell me what sounds you hear.
If there are indescribable monsters
Tell me what they look like but not now.
(Your book entitled *Tackle Pre-History This Way*

Will be of assistance here.)
Perhaps you are cast adrift in a broken barrel
In stormy shark-infested waters
(Remember the work we did on piranhas for RE?)
Try to see yourself. Can you do that?
See yourself at the bottom of a pothole in the Andes
With both legs broken
And your life ebbing away inexorably.
What does the limestone feel like?
See the colours.
Have you done that? Good.
And now you may open your eyes.
Your imagining time is over,
Now it is writing time.
Are we ready to write? Good.
Then write away.
Wayne, you're getting some exciting ideas down.
Tracy, that's lovely.
Darren, you haven't written anything.
Couldn't you put the date?
You can't think of anything to write.
Well, what did you see when you closed your eyes?
But you must have seen something beside the black.
Yes, apart from the little squiggles.
Just the black. I see.
Well, try to think
Of as many words for black as you can.'

Miss Creedle whirls about the class
Like a benign typhoon
Spinning from one quailing homestead to another.
I dream of peaceful ancient days
In Mr Swindell's class
When the hours passed like a dream
Filled with order and measuring and tests.
Excitement is not one of the things I come to school for.
I force my eyes shut
But all I see
Is a boy of twelve
Sitting at a desk one dark November day
Writing this poem
And Darren is happy to discover
There is only one word for black
And that will have to suffice
Until the bell rings for all of us.

The Commentator

Good afternoon and welcome
To this international
Between England and Holland
Which is being played here today
At 4, Florence Terrace.
And the pitch looks in superb condition
As Danny Markey, the England captain,
Puts England on the attack.
Straight away it's Markey
With a lovely little pass to Foden,
Foden back to Markey,
Markey in possession here
Jinking skilfully past the dustbins;
And a neat flick inside the cat there.
What a brilliant player this Markey is
And he's still only nine years old!
Markey to Grealish,
Grealish back to Markey,
Markey is through, he's through,
No, he's been tackled by the drainpipe;
But he's won the ball back brilliantly
And he's advancing on the Dutch keeper,
It must be a goal.
The keeper's off his line
But Markey chips him superbly
And it's a goal
No!

It's gone into Mrs Spence's next door.
And Markey's going round to ask for his ball back,
It could be the end of this international.
Now the door's opening
And yes, it's Mrs Spence,
Mrs Spence has come to the door.
Wait a minute
She's shaking her head, she is shaking her head,
She's not going to let England have their ball back.
What is the referee going to do?
Markey's coming back looking very dejected,
And he seems to be waiting . . .
He's going back,
Markey is going back for that ball!
What a brilliant and exciting move!
He waited until the front door was closed
And then went back for that ball.
And wait a minute,
He's found it, Markey has found that ball,
He has found that ball
And that's wonderful news
For the hundred thousand fans gathered here
Who are showing their appreciation
In no uncertain fashion.
But wait a minute,
The door's opening once more.
It's her, it's Mrs Spence
And she's waving her fist
And shouting something I can't quite understand

But I don't think it's encouragement.
And Markey's off,
He's jinked past her on the outside
Dodging this way and that
With Mrs Spence in hot pursuit.
And he's past her, he's through,
What skills this boy has!
But Mr Spence is there too,
Mr Spence in the sweeper role
With Rover their dog.
Markey's going to have to pull out all the stops now.
He's running straight at him,
And he's down, he's down on all fours!
What is he doing?
And Oh my goodness that was brilliant,
That was absolutely brilliant,
He's dived through Spence's legs;
But he's got him,
This rugged stopper has him by the coat
And Rover's barking in there too;
He'll never get out of this one.
But this is unbelievable!
He's got away
He has got away:
He wriggled out of his coat
And left part of his trousers with Rover.
This boy is real dynamite.
He's over the wall
He's clear

They'll never catch him now.
He's down the yard and on his way
And I don't think we're going to see
Any more of Markey
Until it's safe to come home.

Bird

Something fluttered about my heart
Like a bird caught in a snare
I blame the girl on the fourteen bus
It was she who put it there.

Saturdays

Real
Genuine
Saturdays
Like marbles
Conkers
Sweet new potatoes
Have their especial season
Are all morning
With midday at five o'clock.
True Saturdays
Are borrowed from early Winter
And the left overs
Of Autumn sunshine days
But separate from days of snow.
The skies dine on dwindles of smoke
Where leafy plots smoulder
With small fires.
Sunday meat is bought
And late
Large, white loaves
From little corner shops.
People passing
Wave over garden walls,
Greengrocers and milkmen are smiled upon
And duly paid.
It is time for the chequered tablecloth
And bowls of soup.

And early on
We set out with some purpose
Through only
Lovely Saturday,
Under skies
Like sun-shot water,
For the leccy train
And the Match in Liverpool.

Saturday Night at the Bethlehem Arms

Very quiet really for a Saturday.
Just the old couple come to visit relations
Who took the double room above the yard
And were both of them in bed by half past nine.
Left me with that other one, the stranger.
Sat like he was set till Domesday at the corner of the bar
Sipping small beer dead slow and keeping mum,
Those beady, tax-collector's eyes of his
On my reflection in the glass behind the bar
Watching me, watching me.
And when he did get round to saying something
His talk was like those lines of gossamer
That fishermen send whispering across the water
To lure and hook unwary fish.
Not my type. And anyway I'd been on the go since five.
Dead beat I was.
Some of us have a bed to go to, I thought to myself.

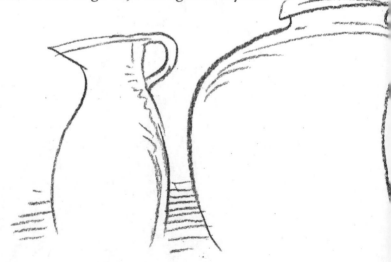

I was just about to call Time
When the knock came at the door.
At first I was for turning them away;
We only have two rooms see and both of them were taken.
But something desperate in the woman's eyes
Made me think again and I told them,
They could rough it in the barn
If they didn't mind the cows and mules for company.
I know, I know. Soft, that's me.
I yawned, locked up, turned out the lights,
Rinsed my hands to lose the smell of beer.
Went up to bed.
A day like any other.
That's how it is.
Nothing much ever happens here.

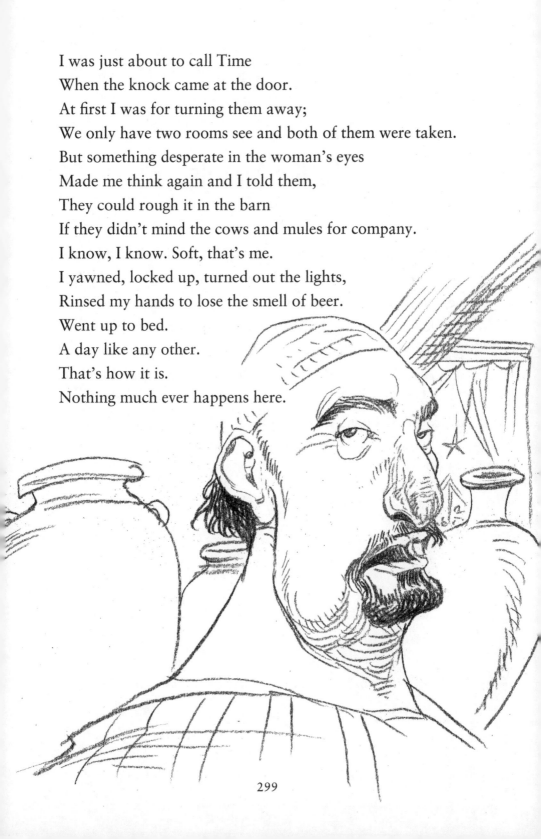

Grace Nichols

Grace Nichols was born in Guyana, West Indies, in 1950. She came to Britain in 1977. Her books include novels for children and adults, and collections of poetry. Her children's books include *Come On In To My Tropical Garden*, *Give Yourself a Hug*, *Paint Me a Poem and Cosmic Disco*. With her partner, John Agard, she co-edited the anthology *Under the Moon and Over the Sea*, which received the first CLPE Children's Poetry Award. In 2021 she won the Queen's Gold Medal for Poetry.

Morning

Morning comes
    with a milk-float jiggling

Morning comes
    with a milkman whistling

Morning comes
    with empties clinking

Morning comes
    with alarm-clock ringing

Morning comes
    with toaster popping

Morning comes
    with letters dropping

Morning comes
    with kettle singing

Morning comes
    with me just listening

Morning comes to drag me out of bed
    – Boss-Woman Morning.

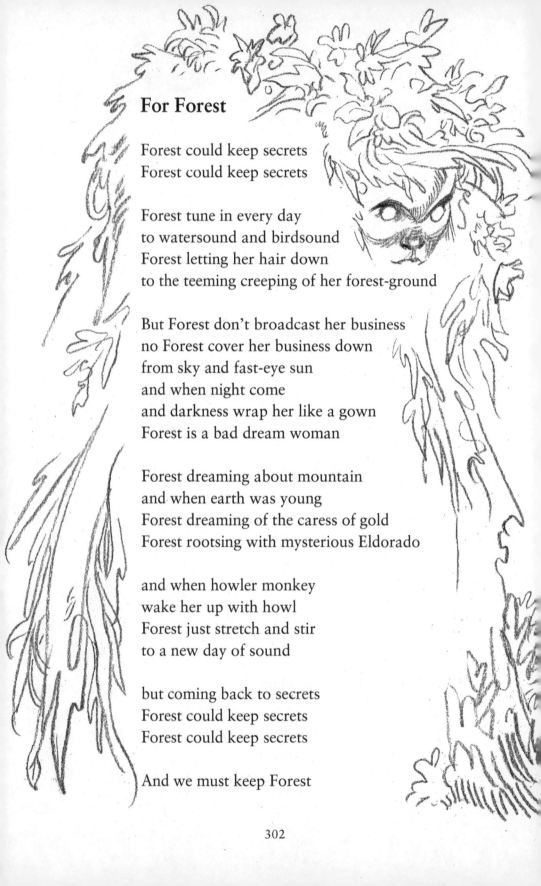

For Forest

Forest could keep secrets
Forest could keep secrets

Forest tune in every day
to watersound and birdsound
Forest letting her hair down
to the teeming creeping of her forest-ground

But Forest don't broadcast her business
no Forest cover her business down
from sky and fast-eye sun
and when night come
and darkness wrap her like a gown
Forest is a bad dream woman

Forest dreaming about mountain
and when earth was young
Forest dreaming of the caress of gold
Forest rootsing with mysterious Eldorado

and when howler monkey
wake her up with howl
Forest just stretch and stir
to a new day of sound

but coming back to secrets
Forest could keep secrets
Forest could keep secrets

And we must keep Forest

Mama-Wata

Down by the seaside
when the moon is in bloom
sits Mama-Wata
gazing up at the moon

She sits as she combs
her hair like a loom
she sits as she croons
a sweet kind of tune

But don't go near Mama-Wata
when the moon is in bloom
for sure she will take you
down to your doom.

Give Yourself a Hug

Give yourself a hug
when you feel unloved

Give yourself a hug
when people put on airs
to make you feel a bug

Give yourself a hug
when everyone seems to give you
a cold-shoulder shrug

Give yourself a hug –
a big big hug

And keep on singing,
'Only one in a million like me
Only one in a million-billion-thrillion-zillion
like me.'

Granny Granny
Please Comb My Hair

Granny Granny please comb my hair
you always take your time
you always take such care

You put me on a cushion between your knees
you rub a little coconut oil
parting gentle as a breeze

Mummy Mummy
she's always in a hurry-hurry
rush
she pulls my hair
sometimes she tugs

But Granny
you have all the time
in the world
and when you're finished
you always turn my head and say
'Now who's a nice girl?'

Tabby

My cat is all concentrated tiger.
I can only imagine the thousands
of millions of years
it must have taken to perfect her.
Growing smaller and smaller
with each evolution.
Growing more and more refined
and even-tempered under her fur.

See how she constantly licks
and grooms herself all over?

A small Queen of Sheba
stamping everywhere her padded
signature – a royal reminder
of the days she was a full-blown tiger.
Older O much older than Egypt.

Now, just look at her –
my grey and black tabby, stepping lightly,
emerging head first from between
the green garden stalks –

Ancient and new as the birth of a star.

Teenage Earthbirds

Flying by
on the winged-wheels
of their heels

Two teenage earthbirds
skate-boarding
down the street

Rising
unfeathered –
in sudden air-leap

Defying law
death and gravity
as they do a wheelie

Landing back
in the smooth swoop
of youth

And faces gaping
gawking, impressed
and unimpressed

Only mother watches – heartbeat in her mouth.

Peter Dixon

Peter Dixon grew up in London during the Second World War. He lived with his mother as his father was away in the army. With no brothers or sisters to play with, or TV and computer screens to google at, Peter became an expert at entertaining himself. Although he didn't like writing at school, he loved writing about his own ideas at home.

Peter became a teacher and lecturer in education. He also painted pictures, made creations on his potter's wheel, scuba-dived, dug the deepest garden pond in town, looked after his tortoise Flash, and wrote poems and stories. When he retired from his job he had even more time to write – recording things that happened and things he imagined had happened. Much of his writing was poetry, some of which Macmillan published.

Magic Cat

My mum whilst walking through the door
spilt some magic on the floor.
Blobs of this
and splots of that
but most of it upon the cat.

Our cat turned magic, straight away
and in the garden went to play
where it grew two massive wings
and flew around in fancy rings.
'Oh look!' cried Mother, pointing high,
'I didn't know our cat could fly.'
Then with a dash of Tibby's tail
she turned my mum into a snail!

So now she lives beneath a stone
and dusts around a different home.
And I'm an ant
and Dad's a mouse
and Tibby's living in our house.

Lone Mission

On evenings, after cocoa
(blackout down and sealed)
I would build plasticine Hamburgs
on green lino
and bomb them with encyclopaedias
(dropped at ceiling level)
from my Lancaster Bomber
built
(usually)
from table, box and curtains
turret made of chairs
radio and gas masks
tray and kitchen ware.
But:

     Aircrew were my problem
     gunners mid and rear
     radio and bomber
     nav. and engineer.

Each night I flew lone missions
through flak both hot and wild
and learnt it wasn't easy
to be an only child.

Grown-Ups

Where are your trainers and where is your coat
Where is your pen and where are your books
Where is the paper and where is the key
Where is the sugar and where is the tea
Where are your socks
Your bag and your hat?
Tidy your room!
Look after the cat!

You're hopeless
Untidy
You lose everything.

Where is your bracelet and where is your ring
Where is your ruler
Hymn book and shoes
Where is your scarf?
You lose and you lose.

You're hopeless
Untidy
You lose everything.

You're careless and casual
You drop and you fling
You're destructive and thoughtless
You don't seem to care

Your coat's on the floor
Your boots on the chair
Why don't you think
Why don't you try
Learn to be helpful; like your father and I.

Mum . . . Dad . . .

Where are the woodlands, the corncrake and the whales
Where are all the dolphins, the tigers and dales
Where are the Indians, the buffalo herds
Fishes and forests and great flying birds

Where are the rivers
Where are the seas
Where are the marshes
And where are the trees

Where is the pure air
Acid-free showers
Where are the moorlands
The meadows and flowers?

These were your treasures
Your keepsakes of time
You've lost them
You've sold them
And they could have been mine.

Poetry Day

Today's a good day.
Poems everywhere
    peeping
    poking
    running
    jumping
– leaping
from every
      hat
      cat
      rat
      dog
      and
      bus shelter.
There are so many I stumble as I step,
squash them as I walk.
I gather a headful
wondering which to immortalize
for you
in ink
and pen
and A4 sheet . . .
    neatly folded.

Love from Pete X

Missing Important Things

I didn't go to school this week
I stayed at home with Dad.
I didn't do a worksheet
and I am really rather glad.
I didn't do the number work,
I didn't do my words,
I didn't learn my spellings
and I didn't read my page.
I didn't go to school today –
we fixed the shed instead,
tied some flies and feathers
and dug the onion bed.
I saw the cat have kittens,
I climbed right up a tree,
mixed some sand and water
and held a bumblebee.
I didn't go to school all week
and I'm really not too sad –
I missed important lessons
and stayed at home with Dad.

Why?

Why do cats
on winter nights
just as the goal of the year is about to be scored
appear at the window?

And why
having spilt tea
and finally
found key
and opened door
do they run away into the darkness?
Leaving me to wonder at their stupidity
and the final score.

The Penguin in the Fridge

Deep within the refrigerator
in the space once occupied
by Grandma's gammon steak
a penguin has built a small nest
(chips and cheese and celery sticks).

It is not an emperor penguin
a king or queen . . .
Not a prince or princess
a lady or lord . . .
No – just an ordinary penguin
with nest and egg
and Grandma's gammon steak.

Clare Bevan

Clare has always loved poetry – and wrote poems at school. So, when she became a primary school teacher, she made sure her classes enjoyed poetry too. She gave her pupils poems and plays to perform – the tiniest child can become a hero!

Now, it was time to challenge herself! So one frosty morning with two cold cats on her lap . . . she began to write. And her first book won a prize! She was a writer at last. Now the poems grew! She was grateful to find such a welcoming circle of friends . . . and publishers too. And she enjoys the fun she has when she visits schools around the country.

It is wonderful to find her poems in a big anthology – and sometimes there's a splendid illustration too!

Clare lives in a cobwebby house, with her husband and plenty of spiders!

She likes dressing up for the village carnival – and looking out for brilliant ideas for new poems.

The Spider

This poem was pinned to a tiny grave under Clare Bevan's hazel tree.

The fairy child loved her spider.

Even when it grew fat
And grey and old,
She would comb its warm fur
With a hazel twig
And take it for slow walks
On its silky lead.

Sometimes it played cat-cradles with her
But more often it wove hammocks
Amongst the long grasses
And they swung together under friendly trees.

When it died,
Her mother bought her a money spider
Who scuttled and tumbled to make her smile.
But it wasn't the same,
And still, when she curls up to sleep
In the lonely dawn,
She murmurs her old spider's name.

The Music Lesson Rap

I'm the bongo kid,
I'm the big-drum-beater,
I'm the click-your-sticks,
I'm the tap-your-feeter.
When the lesson starts,
When we clap our hands,
Then it's me who dreams
Of the boom-boom bands,
And it's me who stamps,
And it's me who yells
For the biff-bang gong,
Or the ding-dong bells,
Or the cymbals (large),
Or the cymbals (small),
Or the tubes that chime
Round the bash-crash hall,
Or the tambourine,
Or the thunder-maker –
But all you give me
Is the sssh-sssh shaker!

Just Doing My Job

I'm one of Herod's Henchmen
We don't have much to say,
We just charge through the audience
In a Henchman sort of way.

We all wear woolly helmets
To hide our hair and ears,
And Wellingtons sprayed silver
To match our tinfoil spears.

Our swords are made of cardboard
So blood will not be spilled
If we trip and stab a parent
When the hall's completely filled.

We don't look very scary,
We're mostly small and shy,
And some of us wear glasses,
But we give the thing a try.

We whisper Henchman noises
While Herod hunts for strangers,
And then we all charge out again
Like nervous Power Rangers.

Yet when the play is over
And Miss is out of breath
We'll charge like Henchmen through the hall
And scare our mums to death.

Literacy Hour

So let's make this clear,
an ADJECTIVE is a
DESCRIBING word . . .
(The long, winding, deep, dark, gloomy, secret
Tunnel leads under
The cold, bare, windy, wet, empty
Playground to the
Wild, wonderful, sunny, exciting, outside
World.)

And a NOUN, of course,
Is an OBJECT, a SUBJECT,
A THING . . .
(If only I had
A glider, or a private jet, or a space rocket,
        or a hot-air balloon, or a time machine,
I could fly away to
The seaside, or the zoo, or a forest, or Egypt,
        or Disneyland, or Anywhere-But-Here.)

A VERB, as we all know,
I hope,
Is a DOING word . . .
(I could run, or race, or tiptoe, or clamber,
        or catapult, or dance, or whirl, or just walk
My way to freedom.)

And an ADVERB tells you
Exactly how the action
Is done . . .
(Joyfully, happily, noisily, silently, timidly,
        bravely, desperately, frantically, urgently,
        nervously, wistfully, longingly, dreamily,
Someday,
Sometime,
Soon.)

Fairy Names

When Clare found this poem, all the names
had been crossed out . . . except for one!

What shall we call the Fairy Child?

Mouse-Fur? Cat's Purr?
Weasel-Wild?

Bat-Wing? Bee-Sting?
Shining River?
Snakebite? Starlight?
Stone? Or Shiver?

Acorn? Frogspawn?
Golden Tree?
Snowflake? Daybreak?
Stormy Sea?

Snail-Shell? Harebell?
Scarlet Flame?

How shall we choose the Fairy's name?

A Flutter of Fairies

Collected by Clare

A flutter of fairies.
A whisper of wings.
A shiver of cobwebs.
A spangle of rings.
A canter of horse flies.
A rumble of bees.
A splatter of frogs.
A city of trees.
A village of toadstools.
An ocean of ponds.
A procession of snails.
A sparkle of wands.
A glimmer of glow-worms.
A treasure of dew.
A shower of wishes
For me. And for you.

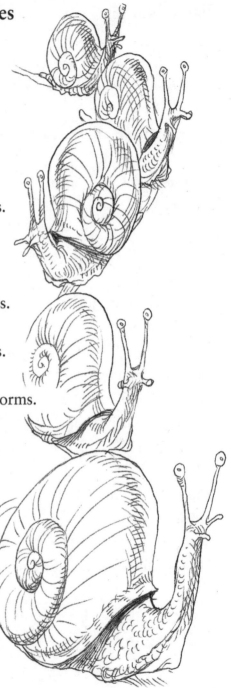

The Mermaid's Garden

*Clare discovered this poem underneath
her seaside spade.*

Her garden far
Beneath the seas
Has shark-tooth fences,
Driftwood trees,
A coral bed of
Crimson flowers,
Seaweed hedges,
Three tall towers
(That once were masts
Of ships, you know!),
A rocky bank
Where starfish glow,
A maze of blue anemones
(That tremble in
The salty breeze),
A marble statue
Old and grand
(She found it buried
In the sand),

A pathway made
From pearly shells
And plants that grow
In broken bells,
While stripy fish
With jewel eyes
Dart about like
Butterflies . . .

(And when you dream
Perhaps you'll creep
Around her garden
In your sleep.)

David Harmer

David Harmer lives with his wife, Paula, in Doncaster with two dogs and a cat. His children have grown up now and live in Rotherham and Leeds. He is a Grandpa for Euan and Jude. For a long time he worked in primary schools, but in 2004 he became a full-time writer. David has written and performed for many years and has had many books published, starting with *Elephant Dreams* in 1998, which he shared with Ian McMillan and Paul Cookson. David worked with Paul Cookson in the performance poetry duo Spill The Beans, which was a lot of fun.

David hopes his poems will make you think a bit, giggle a bit, nod a bit, shake a bit, and then he hopes some of them will make you laugh out loud. When he isn't writing poems, David likes reading, walking with the dogs, watching Sheffield United and eating pies.

My Mum's Put Me on the Transfer List

On Offer:
one nippy striker, ten years old
has scored seven goals this season
has nifty footwork and a big smile
knows how to dive in the penalty box
can get filthy and muddy within two minutes
guaranteed to wreck his kit each week
this is a FREE TRANSFER
but he comes with running expenses
weeks of washing shirts and shorts
socks and vests, a pair of trainers
needs to scoff huge amounts
of chips and burgers, beans and apples
pop and cola, crisps and oranges
endless packets of chewing gum.
This offer open until the end of the season
I'll have him back then
at least until the cricket starts.
Any takers?

South to North; 1965

I was born south of the river
down in the delta, beyond the bayou
lived in the swamps just off the High Street
London alligators snapping my ankles.

It was Bromley, Beckenham, Penge, Crystal Palace
where the kids said *wotcha*, ate bits of *cike*,
the land my father walked as a boy
the land his father walked before him.

I was rooted there, stuck in the clay
until we drove north, moved to Yorkshire
a land of cobbles, coal pits and coke works
forges and steel, fires in the sky.

Where you walked through fields around your village
didn't need three bus-rides to see a farm.

It was Mexborough, Barnsley, Sprotbrough, Goldthorpe
I was deafened by words, my tongue struck dumb
gobsmacked by a language I couldn't speak in.

Ayop, sithee, it's semmers nowt
What's tha got in thi snap, chaze else paze?
Who does tha support, Owls else Blades?
Dun't thee tha me, thee tha thi sen
Tha's a rate 'un thee, giz a spice?

Cheese and peas, sweets and football
I rolled in a richness of newfound vowels
words that dazed, dazzled and danced
out loud in my head until it all made sense
in this different country, far away
from where I was born, south of the river.

Mister Moore

Mister Moore, Mister Moore
Creaking down the corridor.

Uh uh eh eh uh
Uh uh eh eh uh

Mister Moore wears wooden suits
Mister Moore's got great big boots
Mister Moore's got hair like a brush
And Mister Moore don't like me much.

Mister Moore, Mister Moore
Creaking down the corridor.

Uh uh eh eh uh
Uh uh eh eh uh

When my teacher's there I haven't got a care
I can do my sums, I can do gerzinters
When Mister Moore comes through the door
Got a wooden head filled with splinters.

Mister Moore, Mister Moore
Creaking down the corridor.

Uh uh eh eh uh
Uh uh eh eh uh

Mister Moore I implore
My earholes ache, my head is sore
Don't come through that classroom door
Don't come through that classroom door.
Mister Mister Mister Moore
He's creaking down the corridor.

Uh uh eh eh uh
Uh uh eh eh uh

Big voice big hands
Big voice he's a very big man
Take my advice, be good be very very nice
Be good be very very nice
To Mister Moore, Mister Moore
Creaking down the corridor

Uh uh eh eh uh
Uh uh eh eh uh

Mister Moore wears wooden suits
Mister Moore's got great big boots
Mister Moore's got hair like a brush
Mister Moore don't like me much.

Mister Moore, Mister Moore
Creaking down the corridor.

Uh uh eh eh uh
Uh uh eh eh uh

One Moment in Summer

The house is dropping swallows
one by one from under the gutter

they swoop and fall
on our heads as we queue
for ice cream.

It is so hot
that the long line of cars clogging the road
hums like a line of electric fires.

They shine and shimmer, stink of oil and warm seats
the children gaze out from their misted windows.

Trapped under glass
hair plastered down with sweat
gasping for breath like frogs under ice.

The cars crawl round the curve
of the road, stuck in between the shop
and the cafe.

My ice cream is butterscotch and almond
Lizzie's is chocolate, Harriet's vanilla.

They are so delicious and cold
we lick them slowly, letting the long, cool flavours
slide down our tongues.

Inside the cars, the red-faced people
begin to boil.

The swallows flit and dart
rapid specks of blueblack and white
the summer flies at us
like an arrow.

It's Behind You

I don't want to scare you
But just behind you
Is a . . .

No! Don't look!
Just act calmly
As if it wasn't there.

Like I said
Can you hear me if I whisper?
Just behind you
Is a . . .

NO! DON'T LOOK!
Just keep on reading
Don't turn round, believe me
It isn't worth it.

If you could see
What I can see standing there
You'd understand.

335

It's probably one
Of the harmless sort
Although with that mouth
Not to mention the teeth
And all that blood
Dripping down its chin
I wouldn't like to say.

Oh listen
It's trying to speak
I think it wants to be friends.

Oh I see it doesn't, never mind
You'd better leave just in case
I expect you'll escape
If you don't look round.

Oh what a shame!
I thought you'd make it
To the door. Hard luck.
I still think it means no harm
I expect it bites all its friends.

At Cider Mill Farm

I remember my uncle's farm
Still in mid-summer
Heat hazing the air above the red roof tops
Some cattle sheds, a couple of stables
Clustered round a small yard
Lying under the hills that stretched their long back
Through three counties.

I rolled with his dogs
Among the hay bales
Stacked high in the barn he built himself
During a storm one autumn evening
Tunnelled for treasure or jumped with a scream
From a pirate ship's mast into the straw
Burrowed for gold and found he'd buried
Three battered Ford cars deep in the hay.

He drove an old tractor that sweated oil
In long black streaks down the rusty orange
It chugged and whirred, coughed into life
Each day as he clattered across the cattle grids
I remember one night my cousin and I
Dragging back cows from over the common
We prodded the giant steaming flanks
Pushed them homeward through the rain
And then drank tea from huge tin mugs
Feeling like farmers.

He's gone now, he sold it
But I have been back for one last look
To the twist in the lane that borders the stream
Where Mary, Ruth and I once waded
Water sloshing over our wellies
And I showed my own children my uncle's farm,
The barn still leaning over the straw,
With for all I know three battered Ford cars
Still buried beneath it.

The Bubble Between Two Buildings

Wet petals stick ragged pink splodges
onto the path
        that twists and wriggles
under my feet like a long black snake.

The wind is warm, I can smell
blossom as it bends on its branches
watch it fly
        in a shower of flowers
scattered into the rain spattering down.

I'm stuck in a bubble between two buildings
my arms full of registers, messages, parcels
all the classrooms
        buzz like beehives full of bustle
children and grown-ups all painting and writing
talking and thinking, laughing and singing
chattering, shouting, counting and weighing.

339

Outside I can hear
the milk float droning down our street
the other side of the fence
        two dogs barking
and birds singing in the hedge by the path.

It's still and calm
breathing the blossom-heavy air
I lean into the warm, wet wind
        wait for my feet
to lead me back to my busy classroom
down the shining tarmac painted with blossom.

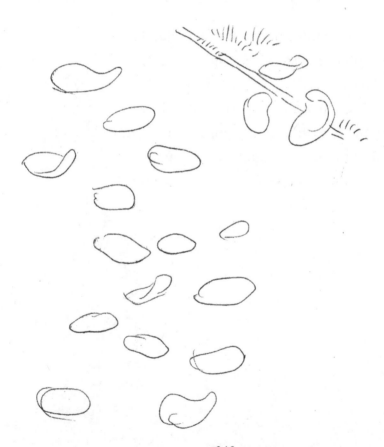

Eleanor Farjeon

Eleanor Farjeon was one of the most important children's writers of the twentieth century. She published over eighty books of poetry, short stories, novels, plays including a childhood autobiography *A Nursery in the Nineties* and a memoir of her friendship with Edward Thomas, *The Last Four Years*. In 1956 she was awarded the Carnegie and Hans Andersen Medals and in 1959 the Regina Medal from the United States.

The Eleanor Farjeon Award is presented annually, in her memory, for outstanding service to children's literature. Macmillan published *Blackbird Has Spoken: Selected Poems for Children* in 1999.

Cats

Cats sleep
Anywhere,
Any table,
Any chair,
Top of piano,
Window-ledge,
In the middle,
On the edge,
Open drawer,
Empty shoe,
Anybody's
Lap will do,
Fitted in a
Cardboard box,
In the cupboard
With your frocks –
Anywhere!
They don't care!
Cats sleep
Anywhere.

It Was Long Ago

I'll tell you, shall I, something I remember?
Something that still means a great deal to me.
It was long ago.

A dusty road in summer I remember,
A mountain and an old house, and a tree
That stood, you know,

Behind the house. An old woman I remember
In a red shawl with a grey cat on her knee
Humming under a tree.

She seemed the oldest thing I can remember,
But then perhaps I was not more than three.
It was long ago.

I dragged on the dusty road, and I remember
How the old woman looked over the fence at me
And seemed to know

How it felt to be three, and called out, I remember,
'Do you like bilberries and cream for tea?'
I went under the tree

And while she hummed, and the cat purred, I remember
How she filled a saucer with berries and cream for me
So long ago,

Such berries and such cream as I remember
I never had seen before, and never see
Today, you know.

And that is almost all I can remember,
The house, the mountain, the grey cat on her knee,
Her red shawl, and the tree,
And the taste of the berries, the feel of the sun I remember,
And the smell of everything that used to be
So long ago,

Till the heat on the road outside again I remember,
And how the long dusty road seemed to have for me
No end, you know.

That is the farthest thing I can remember.
It won't mean much to you. It does to me.
Then I grew up, you see.

The Night Will Never Stay

The night will never stay,
The night will still go by,
Though with a million stars
You pin it to the sky;
Though you bind it with the blowing wind
And buckle it with the moon,
The night will slip away
Like sorrow or a tune.

Argus and Ulysses

Argus was a puppy,
Frisking full of joy.
Ulysses was his master,
Who sailed away to Troy.

Argus on the sea-shore
Watched the ship's white track,
And barked a little puppy-bark
To bring his master back.

Argus was an old dog,
Too grey and tired for tears,
He lay outside the house-door
And watched for twenty years.

When twenty years were ended
Ulysses came from Troy.
Argus wagged an old dog's wag,
And then he died for joy.

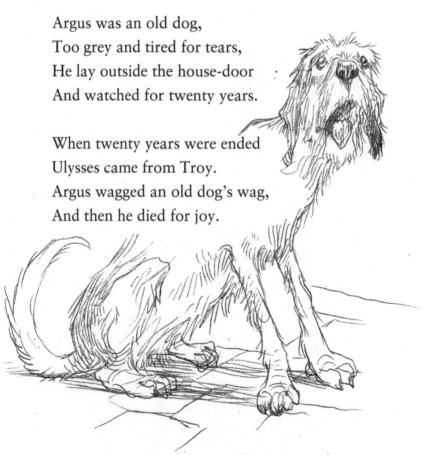

Henry VIII
1509

Bluff King Hal was full of beans;
He married half a dozen queens;
For three called Kate they cried the banns,
And one called Jane, and a couple of Annes.

The first he asked to share his reign
Was Kate of Aragon, straight from Spain –
But when his love for her was spent,
He got a divorce, and out she went.

Anne Boleyn was his second wife;
He swore to cherish her all his life –
But seeing a third he wished instead,
He chopped off poor Anne Boleyn's head.

He married the next afternoon
Jane Seymour, which was rather soon –
But after one year as his bride
She crept into her bed and died.

347

Anne of Cleves was Number Four;
Her portrait thrilled him to the core –
But when he met her face to face
Another royal divorce took place.

Catherine Howard, Number Five,
Billed and cooed to keep alive –
But one day Henry felt depressed;
The executioner did the rest.

Sixth and last came Catherine Parr,
Sixth and last and luckiest far –
For this time it was Henry who
Hopped the twig, and a good job too.

A Morning Song

For the First Day of Spring

Morning has broken
Like the first morning,
Blackbird has spoken
    Like the first bird.
Praise for the singing!
Praise for the morning!
Praise for them, springing
    From the first Word.

Sweet the rain's new fall
Sunlit from heaven,
Like the first dewfall
    In the first hour.
Praise for the sweetness
Of the wet garden,
Sprung in completeness
    From the first shower.

Mine is the sunlight!
Mine is the morning
Born of the one light
    Eden saw play.
Praise with elation,
Praise every morning
Spring's re-creation
    Of the First Day!

Christmas Stocking

What will go into the Christmas Stocking
While the clock on the mantelpiece goes tick-tocking?
    An orange, a penny,
    Some sweets, not too many,
    A trumpet, a dolly,
    A spring of red holly,
    A book and a top
    And a grocery shop,
    Some beads in a box,
    An ass and an ox
    And a lamb, plain and good,
    All whittled in wood,
    A white sugar dove,
    A handful of love,
    Another of fun,
    And it's very near done –
    A big silver star
    On top – there you are!
Come morning you'll wake to the clock's tick-tocking,
And that's what you'll find in the Christmas Stocking.

Ian McMillan

Ian McMillan is a writer and broadcaster who presents The Verb on BBC Radio 3 every Friday night. He's written poems, plays, and a verse autobiography. He is poet-in-residence for The Academy of Urbanism, Barnsley FC and is now Barnsley's Lockdown Poet. He has explored language and communication with schoolchildren, students, teachers, education policy makers, politicians, public services and corporate businesses, in every conceivable location, from an archaeological dig to a Swiss mountain railway.

Ready Salted

Nothing else happened
that day.

Nothing much, anyway.

I got up, went to school,
did the usual stuff.

Came home, watched telly,
did the usual stuff.

Nothing else happened
that day,

nothing much, anyway,

but the eyeball in the crisps
was enough.

Counting the Stars

It's late at night
and John is counting the stars.

He's walking through the woods
and counting the stars.

The night is clear
and the stars are like salt

on a black tablecloth.
John counts silently,

his lips moving, his head tilted.
It's late at night

and John is counting the stars
until he walks into a tree

that he never saw
because he was counting the stars.

Look at John
lying in the woods.

The woodland creatures are gathering around him
laughing

in little woodland voices.

Moral:
Even when you're looking up,
Don't forget to look down.

Routes

1. The Walk to School

Down Barking-dog Lane
past the street with the boat
  Clouds rush by
  Sometimes it rains

Up Old-lady-waving Road
past the field with the car
  Clouds hang still
  Aeroplanes drone

Down Skateboard Steps
past the shop with the cat
  Clouds make shapes
  Reflect in windowpanes

2. The Drive to School

radio shouts
Mum shouts
belt tight
window steam
Dad shouts
radio shouts
feel hot
feel sick
radio, Mum,
Dad shout
shout shout
every day
same shout
same hot
same sick
same same
same same

Ten Things Found in a Shipwrecked Sailor's Pocket

A litre of sea.
An unhappy jellyfish.
A small piece of a lifeboat.
A pencil wrapped around with seaweed.
A soaking feather.
The first page of a book called *Swimming is Easy*.
A folded chart showing dangerous rocks.
A photograph of a little girl in a red dress.
A gold coin.
A letter from a mermaid.

Robinson Crusoe's Wise Sayings

You can never have too many turtles' eggs.
I'm the most interesting person in this room.
A beard is as long as I want it to be.

The swimmer on his own doesn't need trunks.
A tree is a good clock.
If you talk to a stone long enough you'll fall asleep.

I know it's Christmas because I cry.
Waving at ships is useless.
Footprints make me happy, unless they're my own.

The Music I Like

The Music I like
Is very special music.

At this moment,
For instance,

I'm listening to the washing machine
Slowing down,

As the gerbil rattles
In its cage,

And my wife runs
Up the stairs

And my next-door neighbour
Cuts his grass.

Music, very special music
Just listen . . .

Ten One-Line Poems about Sport

Golf
That white moon in the blue sky, orbiting.

Cricket
Long late-afternoon shadows as the bowler runs.

Basketball
The clock runs down slower than the players.

Swimmers
Moment of stillness before the start: water-mirror.

Snooker
The giant's necklace broke and the beads fell on to the grass.

Football
This net's for catching slippery goalfish!

Marathon
Last metre: the best and the worst.

Rugby
Flying Easter egg under the H

High Jump
The air holds me like a hand, then lets me go.

Cycling
Here come the fastest paper boys and girls in the world!

Lewis Carroll

Charles Lutwidge Dodgson, otherwise known as Lewis Carroll, was the son of a vicar and spent his childhood in Cheshire and Yorkshire. It was at Oxford University that he wrote his famous books about Alice, and it is the poems that can be found in the Alice books that are his most humorous and popular.

Jabberwocky

'Twas brillig, and the slithy toves
  Did gyre and gimble in the wabe;
All mimsy were the borogoves,
  And the mome raths outgrabe.

'Beware the Jabberwock, my son!
  The jaws that bite, the claws that catch!
Beware the Jubjub bird, and shun
  The frumious Bandersnatch!'

He took his vorpal sword in hand:
  Long time the manxome foe he sought –
So rested he by the Tumtum tree,
  And stood awhile in thought.

And as in uffish thought he stood,
  The Jabberwock, with eyes of flame,
Came whiffling through the tulgey wood,
  And burbled as it came!

One, two! One, two! And through and through
  The vorpal blade went snicker-snack!
He left it dead, and with its head
  He went galumphing back.

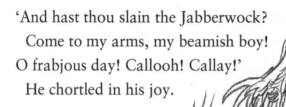

'And hast thou slain the Jabberwock?
  Come to my arms, my beamish boy!
O frabjous day! Callooh! Callay!'
  He chortled in his joy.

'Twas brillig, and the slithy toves
  Did gyre and gimble in the wabe;
All mimsy were the borogoves,
  And the mome raths outgrabe.

Twinkle, Twinkle, Little Bat

Twinkle, twinkle, little bat!
How I wonder what you're at!
Up above the world you fly,
Like a tea-tray in the sky.
  Twinkle, twinkle –
Twinkle, twinkle, twinkle, twinkle.

You Are Old, Father William

'You are old, Father William,' the young man said,
'And your hair has become very white;
And yet you incessantly stand on your head –
Do you think, at your age, it is right?'

'In my youth,' Father William replied to his son,
'I feared it might injure the brain;
But, now that I'm perfectly sure I have none,
Why, I do it again and again.'

'You are old,' said the youth, 'as I mentioned before,
And have grown most uncommonly fat;
Yet you turned a back-somersault in at the door –
Pray, what is the reason of that?'

'In my youth,' said the sage, as he shook his grey locks,
'I kept all my limbs very supple
By the use of this ointment – one shilling the box –
Allow me to sell you a couple?'

'You are old,' said the youth, 'and your jaws are too weak
For anything tougher than suet;
Yet you finished the goose, with the bones and the beak –
Pray, how did you manage to do it?'

'In my youth,' said his father, 'I took to the law,
And argued each case with my wife;
And the muscular strength, which it gave to my jaw,
Has lasted the rest of my life.'

'You are old,' said the youth, 'one would hardly suppose
That your eye was as steady as ever;
Yet you balanced an eel on the end of your nose –
What made you so awfully clever?'

'I have answered three questions, and that is enough,'
Said his father. 'Don't give yourself airs!
Do you think I can listen all day to such stuff?
Be off, or I'll kick you downstairs!'

The Lobster-Quadrille

'Will you walk a little faster?' said a whiting to a snail,
'There's a porpoise close behind us, and he's treading on my
    tail.
See how eagerly the lobsters and the turtles all advance!
They are waiting on the shingle – will you come and join the
    dance?
    Will you, won't you, will you, won't you, will you join the
    dance?
    Will you, won't you, will you, won't you, won't you join
    the dance?

'You can really have no notion how delightful it will be
When they take us up and throw us, with the lobsters, out to
    sea!'
But the snail replied 'Too far, too far!' and gave a look
    askance –
Said he thanked the whiting kindly; but he would not join the
    dance.
    Would not, could not, would not, could not, would not
    join the dance.
    Would not, could not, would not, could not, could not
    join the dance.

'What matters it how far we go?' his scaly friend replied.
'There is another shore, you know, upon the other side.
The further off from England the nearer is to France –
Then turn not pale, beloved snail, but come and join the
   dance.
   Will you, won't you, will you, won't you, will you join the
   dance?
   Will you, won't you, will you, won't you, won't you join
   the dance?'

How doth the little crocodile

How doth the little crocodile
   Improve his shining tail,
And pour the waters of the Nile
   On every golden scale!

How cheerfully he seems to grin,
   How neatly spreads his claws,
And welcomes little fishes in
   With gently smiling jaws!

The Walrus and the Carpenter

The sun was shining on the sea,
Shining with all his might:
He did his very best to make
The billows smooth and bright –
And this was odd, because it was
The middle of the night.

The moon was shining sulkily,
Because she thought the sun
Had got no business to be there
After the day was done –
'It's very rude of him,' she said,
'To come and spoil the fun!'

The sea was wet as wet could be,
The sands were dry as dry.
You could not see a cloud, because
No cloud was in the sky:
No birds were flying overhead –
There were no birds to fly.

The Walrus and the Carpenter
Were walking close at hand;
They wept like anything to see
Such quantities of sand;
'If this were only cleared away,'
They said, 'it *would* be grand!'

'If seven maids with seven mops
Swept it for half a year,
Do you suppose,' the Walrus said,
'That they could get it clear?'
'I doubt it,' said the Carpenter,
And shed a bitter tear.

'O Oysters, come and walk with us!'
The Walrus did beseech.
'A pleasant walk, a pleasant talk,
Along the briny beach:
We cannot do with more than four,
To give a hand to each.'

The eldest Oyster looked at him,
But never a word he said:
The eldest Oyster winked his eye,
And shook his heavy head –
Meaning to say he did not choose
To leave the oyster-bed.

But four young Oysters hurried up,
All eager for the treat:
Their coats were brushed, their faces washed,
Their shoes were clean and neat –
And this was odd, because, you know,
They hadn't any feet.

Four other Oysters followed them,
And yet another four;
And thick and fast they came at last,
And more, and more, and more –
All hopping through the frothy waves,
And scrambling to the shore.

The Walrus and the Carpenter
Walked on a mile or so,
And then they rested on a rock
Conveniently low:
And all the little Oysters stood
And waited in a row.

'The time has come,' the Walrus said,
'To talk of many things:
Of shoes – and ships – and sealing wax –
Of cabbages – and kings –
And why the sea is boiling hot –
And whether pigs have wings.'

'But wait a bit,' the Oysters cried,
'Before we have our chat;
For some of us are out of breath,
And all of us are fat!'
'No hurry!' said the Carpenter.
They thanked him much for that.

'A loaf of bread,' the Walrus said,
'Is what we chiefly need;
Pepper and vinegar besides
Are very good indeed –
Now, if you're ready, Oysters dear,
We can begin to feed.'

'But not on us,' the Oysters cried,
Turning a little blue.
'After such kindness that would be
A dismal thing to do!'
'The night is fine,' the Walrus said,
'Do you admire the view?'

'It was so kind of you to come,
And you are very nice!'
The Carpenter said nothing but,
'Cut us another slice.
I wish you were not quite so deaf –
I've had to ask you twice!'

'It seems a shame,' the Walrus said,
'To play them such a trick.
After we've brought them out so far
And made them trot so quick!'
The Carpenter said nothing but,
'The butter's spread too thick!'

'I weep for you,' the Walrus said,
'I deeply sympathize.'
With sobs and tears he sorted out
Those of the largest size,
Holding his pocket-handkerchief
Before his streaming eyes.

'O Oysters,' said the Carpenter,
'You've had a pleasant run!
Shall we be trotting home again?'
But answer came there none –
And this was scarcely odd, because
They'd eaten every one.

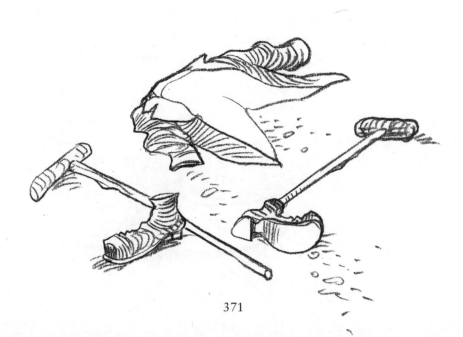

Beautiful Soup

Beautiful Soup, so rich and green,
    Waiting in a hot tureen!
Who for such dainties would not stoop?
Soup of the evening, beautiful Soup!
Soup of the evening, beautiful Soup!
    Beau-ootiful Soo-oop!
    Beau-ootiful Soo-oop!
Soo-oop of the e-e-evening,
    Beautiful, beautiful Soup!

Beautiful Soup! Who cares for fish,
    Game, or any other dish?
Who would not give all else for two
pennyworth only of beautiful Soup?
Pennyworth only of beautiful Soup?
    Beau-ootiful Soo-oop!
    Beau-ootiful Soo-oop!
Soo-oop of the e-e-evening,
    Beautiful, beauti-FUL SOUP!

Jackie Kay

Jackie Kay was born and brought up in Scotland. She writes poetry, novels and short stories for children and adults including *The Frog Who Dreamed She Was an Opera Singer*, winner of the 1999 Signal Award.

She teaches Creative Writing at Newcastle University and is a Fellow of the Royal Society of Literature. From 2016–2021 She was the Makar or National Poet for Scotland.

The Moon at Knowle Hill

The moon was married last night
and nobody saw
dressed up in her ghostly dress
for the summer ball.

The stars shimmied in the sky
and danced a whirligig;
the moon vowed to be true
and lit up the corn-rigs.

She kissed the dark lips of the sky
Above the summer house
She in her pale white dress
swooned across the vast sky

The moon was married last night
the beautiful belle of the ball
and nobody saw her at all
except a small girl in a navy dress

who witnessed it all.

Brendon Gallacher

For my brother, Maxie

He was seven and I was six, my Brendon Gallacher.
He was Irish and I was Scottish, my Brendon Gallacher.
His father was in prison; he was a cat burglar.
My father was a communist party full-time worker.
He had six brothers and I had one, my Brendon Gallacher.

He would hold my hand and take me by the river
Where we'd talk all about his family being poor.
He'd get his mum out of Glasgow when he got older.
A wee holiday some place nice. Some place far.
I'd tell my mum about my Brendon Gallacher

How his mum drank and his daddy was a cat burglar.
And she'd say, 'why not have him round to dinner?'
No, no, I'd say, he's got big holes in his trousers.
I like meeting him by the burn in the open air.
Then one day after we'd been friends two years,

One day when it was pouring and I was indoors,
My mum says to me, 'I was talking to Mrs Moir
Who lives next door to your Brendon Gallacher
Didn't you say his address was 24 Novar?
She says there are no Gallachers at 24 Novar

There never have been any Gallachers next door.'
And he died then, my Brendon Gallacher,
Flat out on my bedroom floor, his spiky hair,
His impish grin, his funny flapping ear.
Oh Brendon, Oh my Brendon Gallacher.

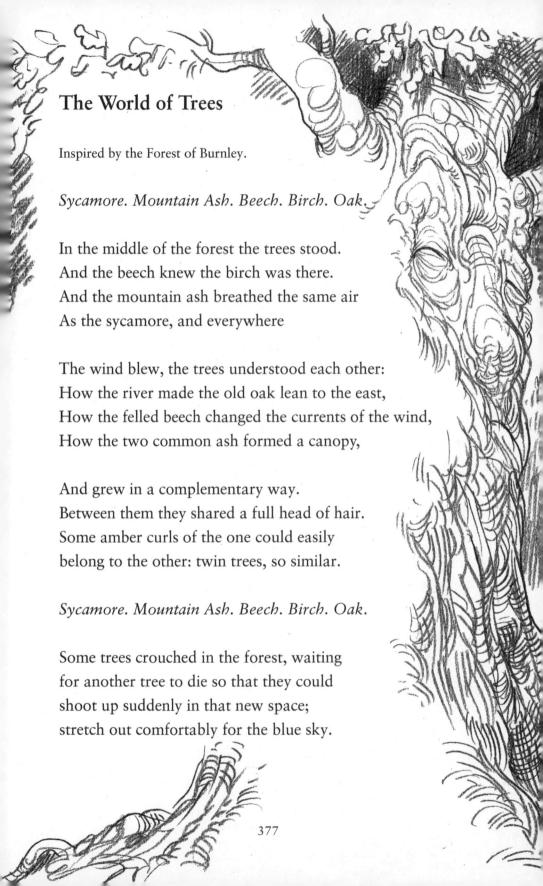

The World of Trees

Inspired by the Forest of Burnley.

Sycamore. Mountain Ash. Beech. Birch. Oak.

In the middle of the forest the trees stood.
And the beech knew the birch was there.
And the mountain ash breathed the same air
As the sycamore, and everywhere

The wind blew, the trees understood each other:
How the river made the old oak lean to the east,
How the felled beech changed the currents of the wind,
How the two common ash formed a canopy,

And grew in a complementary way.
Between them they shared a full head of hair.
Some amber curls of the one could easily
belong to the other: twin trees, so similar.

Sycamore. Mountain Ash. Beech. Birch. Oak.

Some trees crouched in the forest, waiting
for another tree to die so that they could
shoot up suddenly in that new space;
stretch out comfortably for the blue sky.

Some trees grew mysterious mushroom fungi,
shoelace, honey, intricate as a grandmother's lace.
The wind fluttered the leaves; the leaves flapped their wings.
Birds flew from the trees. Sometimes they'd sing.

The tall trees, compassionate, understood everything:
Grief – they stood stock still, branches drooped in despair.
Fear – they exposed their many roots, tugged their gold hair.
Anger – they shook in the storm, pointed their bony fingers.

Sycamore. Mountain Ash. Beech. Birch. Oak.

The trees knew each other's secrets.
In the deep green heart of the forest.
Each tree loved another tree best.
Each tree, happy to rest, leant a little to the east,

Or to the west, when the moon loomed high above,
the big white eye of the woods.
And they stood together as one in the dark,
with the stars sparkling from their branches,

Completely at ease, breathing in the cold night air
swishing a little in the breeze,
dreaming of glossy spring leaves
in the fine, distinguished company of trees.

Sycamore. Mountain Ash. Beech. Birch. Oak.

Sassenachs

Me and my best pal (well, she was
till a minute ago) are off to London.
First trip on an intercity alone.
When we got on we were the same
kind of excited – jigging on our seats,
staring at everyone. But then,
I remembered I had to be sophisticated.
So when Jenny started shouting,
'Look at that, the land's flat already,'
when we were just outside Glasgow
(Motherwell actually) I'd feel myself flush.
Or even worse, 'Sassenach country!
Wey Hey Hey.' The tartan tammy
sitting proudly on top of her pony;
the tartan scarf swinging like a tail.
The nose pressed to the window.
'England's not so beautiful, is it?'
And we haven't even crossed the border!
And the train's jazzy beat joins her:
Sassenachs Sassenachs here we come.
Sassenachs Sassenachs Rum Tum Tum
Sassenachs Sassenachs How do you do.
Sassenachs Sassenachs WE'LL GET YOU.

Then she loses momentum, so out come
the egg mayonnaise sandwiches and
the big bottle of Bru. 'My ma's done us proud,'
says Jenny, digging in, munching loud.
The whole train is an egg and I'm inside it.
I try to remain calm; Jenny starts it again,
Sassenachs Sassenachs Rum Tum Tum.

Finally we get there: London, Euston;
and the first person on the platform
gets asked – 'Are you a genuine Sassenach?'
I want to die, but instead I say, *'Jenny!'*
He replies in that English way –
'I beg your pardon,' and Jenny screams
'Did you hear that Voice?'
And we both die laughing, clutching
our stomachs at Euston.

Grandpa's Soup

No one makes soup like my Grandpa's,
with its diced carrots the perfect size
and its diced potatoes the perfect size
and its wee soft bits –
what are their names?
and its big bit of hough,
which rhymes with loch, floating
like a rich island in the middle of the soup sea.

I say, Grandpa, Grandpa your soup is the best
      soup in the whole world.
And Grandpa says, Och,
which rhymes with hough and loch,
Och, don't be daft,
because he's shy about his soup, my Grandpa.
He knows I will grow up and pine for it.
I will fall ill and desperately need it.
I will long for it my whole life after he is gone.
Every soup will become sad and wrong after he is gone.
He knows when I'm older I will avoid soup altogether.
Oh Grandpa, Grandpa, why is your soup so glorious? I say
tucking into my fourth bowl in a day.

Barley! That's the name of the wee soft bits.
Barley.

Promise

Remember, the time of year
when the future appears
like a blank sheet of paper
a clean calendar, a new chance.
On thick white snow

you vow fresh footprints
then watch them go
with the wind's hearty gust.
Fill your glass. Here's tae us. Promises
made to be broken, made to last.

Vault

After Marion Coutts, 'For the Fallen'

And just when we thought, when we thought, when we thought
      We could not   we could not
      We did, we did   we leapt, we leapt
      We made it   across, across.
      We fell often   were broken; we lost.
      The past is a leap   in the dark: a dark horse.
      We laughed. We wept. Of course, of course.

Colin West

Colin was born in Epping in 1951 and has loved funny songs and rhymes for as long as he can remember. His mum read him Edward Lear's *The Owl and the Pussycat*, which set him on the path to Nonsense Verse. His first book, *Out of the Blue from Nowhere*, was published shortly after he left art college. One character he created, Monty, the Dog who wears Glasses, was made into a BBC cartoon series. Although officially retired, I still enjoy thinking up poems to make people laugh!

Joker

I am the Joker in the pack
The card who makes you smile.
I'm not like King or Queen or Jack,
I am the Joker in the pack –
The cheeky one who answers back
And tells you all the while:
'I am the Joker in the pack,
The card who makes you smile.'

Pogo Stick

Upon my pogo stick I pounce
And out of school I homeward bounce.
I bounce so high, how my heart pounds
until at last I'm out of bounds.

My Colours

These are
My colours,
One by one:

Red –
The poppies
Where I run.

Orange –
Summer's
Setting sun.

Yellow –
Farmers'
Fields of corn.

Green –
The clover
On my lawn.

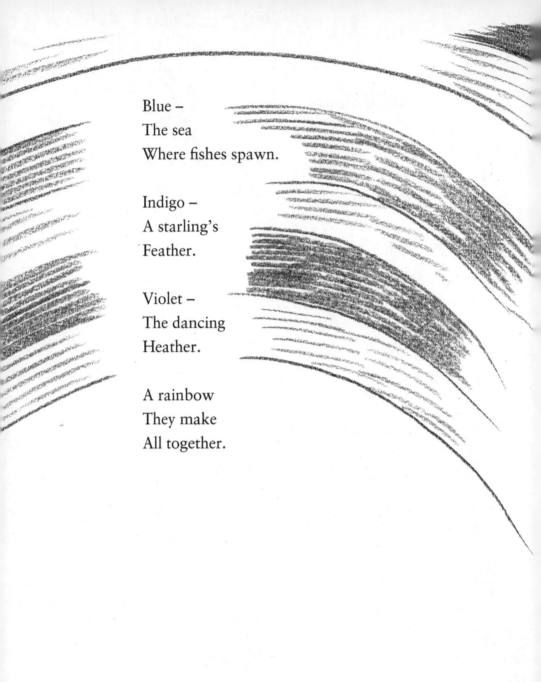

Blue –
The sea
Where fishes spawn.

Indigo –
A starling's
Feather.

Violet –
The dancing
Heather.

A rainbow
They make
All together.

My Sister Sybil

Sipping soup, my sister Sybil
Seems inclined to drool and dribble.
If it wasn't for this foible,
Meal-times would be more enjoible!

King Arthur's Knights

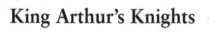

King Arthur's knights were chivalrous
When sat around his table,
But even they were frivolous
Whenever they were able,
And in the moat at Camelot
They splashed about and swam a lot.

Is Reading Aloud . . . ?

Is reading aloud
in this library allowed,
or is reading aloud
not allowed?

Well, reading aloud
is allowed in this library –

AS LONG AS IT
ISN'T TOO LOUD.

Some Stuff in a Sack

One summer's day at half past three
Old Ginger Tom went off to sea,
With some stuff in a sack,
And a parrot called Jack,
Sing Fiddle-dee-fiddle-dee-dee

Beneath the sun he dozed a while,
Then woke up by a desert isle,
With some stuff in a sack,
Like two boots big and black,
And a parrot called Jack,
Sing Fiddle-dee-fiddle-dee-dee.

He crossed a jungle dark and dim
And nothing seemed to bother him,
With some stuff in a sack,
Like a drum he could whack,
And a parrot called Jack.
Sing Fiddle-dee-fiddle-dee-dee

He gathered wood beside a lake
And built a life and took a break,
With some stuff in a sack,
Like a fish finger snack,
And a parrot called Jack,
Sing Fiddle-dee-fiddle-dee-dee.

He met a fearsome pirate crew
But knew exactly what to do,
With some stuff in a sack,
Like a whip that went crack,
And a parrot called Jack,
Sing Fiddle-dee-fiddle-dee-dee.

And then he walked along the shore
And thought he'd put to sea once more,
With some stuff in a sack,
Like a map to get back,
And a parrot called Jack,
Sing Fiddle-dee-fiddle-dee-dee.

And when there came a mighty storm,
Old Ginger Tom slept snug and warm
With some stuff in a sack,
Like a waterproof mac,
And a parrot called Jack,
Sing Fiddle-dee-fiddle-dee-dee.

He woke up when the storm had passed
And saw that he was home at last,
With no stuff in the sack
(Nothing left to unpack),

Sing Fiddle-dee-fiddle-dee-dee.

And all next day the tale he told
Of Tom's Adventures, Brave and Bold
With some stuff in a sack,
Like two boots big and black,
And a drum he could whack,
And a fish finger snack,
And a whip that went crack,
And a map to get back,
And a waterproof mac,
But that parrot called Jack
Sang: FIDDLE-DEE-FIDDLE-DEE-DEE!

Brian Bilston

Brian Bilston has been described as Twitter's unofficial Poet Laureate. With over 300,000 followers on social media, including Roger McGough and Frank Cottrell Boyce, Brian has become truly beloved by the online community. He has published two collections of poetry, *You Took the Last Bus Home* and *Alexa, what is there to know about love?*, and his novel *Diary of a Somebody* was shortlisted for the Costa first novel award. He has also published a collection of football poetry, *50 Ways to Score a Goal*, and his acclaimed poem *Refugees* has been made into an illustrated book for children. Brian's latest collection, *Days Like These*, featuring a poem for every day of the year, publishes this year.

A Brief History of Modern Art in Poetry

1. Impressionism
Roses sway in softened reds
Violets swim in murky blues.
Sugar sparkles in the light,
Blurring into golden you.

2. Surrealism
Roses are melting
Violets are too.
Ceci n'est pas le sucre.
Keith is a giant crab.

3. Abstract Expressionism

4. Social Realism
Roses are dead.
Violence is rife.
Don't sugarcoat
This bitter life.

5. Pop Art
Roses go BLAM!
Violets go POW!
Sugar is COOL!
You are so WOW!

6. Conceptual Art
Roses are red,
Coated in blood:
A deer's severed head
Drips from above.

Refugees

They have no need of our help
So do not tell me
These haggard faces could belong to you or me
Should life have dealt a different hand
We need to see them for who they really are
Chancers and scroungers
Layabouts and loungers
With bombs up their sleeves
Cut-throats and thieves
They are not
Welcome here
We should make them
Go back to where they came from
They cannot
Share our food
Share our homes
Share our countries
Instead let us
Build a wall to keep them out
It is not okay to say
These are people just like us
A place should only belong to those who are born there
Do not be so stupid to think that
The world can be looked at another way

Now read from bottom to top

394

International Cats

International cats
assert their right to relax
in international laps
at any time of day or night.
If denied, they will cite
the Universal Declaration of Feline Rights.

International cats
sit on international mats
that proclaim WELCOME
in each of the world's languages.
International cats can sleep
in up to seven different languishes.

International cats,
proud flouters of human orders,
support cat comrades across borders.
They extend the paw of friendship
to cats who flee catastrophe,
terror and adversity.

LIBERTY, EQUALITY, CATERNITY!

Penguin Awareness

I've been aware of penguins since I was three:
I think one may have moved in with me.

The signs are everywhere.
The smell of saltwater in the air.
There are moulted feathers on my chair
Yesterday I found a fish upon the stair.
But when I turn around there's no one there,
for he moves in the shadows, like Tony Soprano;
I am forever stepping in guano.

I don't know why he's come to live with me.
There are better places for him to be.
But when I've gone to bed, I can hear the tread
of his soft heels across the kitchen floor,
and the opening of the freezer door.

And I picture him there,
his head resting on a frozen shelf,
dreaming sadly of somewhere else,
thinking about the hand that life has dealt him,
and I wonder if his heart is melting.

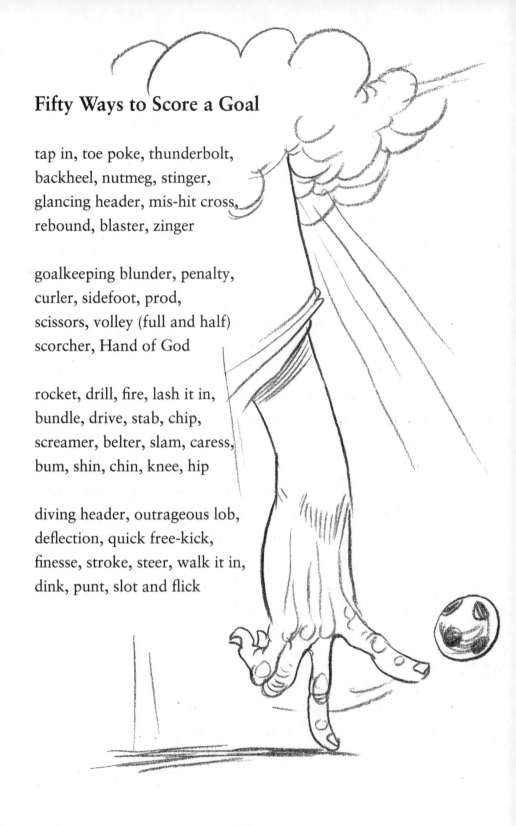

Fifty Ways to Score a Goal

tap in, toe poke, thunderbolt,
backheel, nutmeg, stinger,
glancing header, mis-hit cross,
rebound, blaster, zinger

goalkeeping blunder, penalty,
curler, sidefoot, prod,
scissors, volley (full and half)
scorcher, Hand of God

rocket, drill, fire, lash it in,
bundle, drive, stab, chip,
screamer, belter, slam, caress,
bum, shin, chin, knee, hip

diving header, outrageous lob,
deflection, quick free-kick,
finesse, stroke, steer, walk it in,
dink, punt, slot and flick

The Laws of the Game (Playground edition)

1. The field of play must be a wholly natural playing surface;
   it should be rectangular and marked with continuous lines
   OR
   it can be a peculiarly shaped strip of unforgiving tarmac,
   bordered on one side by the new science block, and the
   bicycle racks on the other.

2. The penalty spot should be situated 10.97m (12yds) from
   the midpoint between the goalposts
   OR
   about 6 paces from the goal line (4½ paces if you're
   Kieran Thomas because he's got really long legs and his
   strides are MASSIVE).

3. A goal consists of two vertical posts joined by a horizontal
   crossbar. The distance between the inside of the posts is
   7.32m (8yds) and the distance from the crossbar to the
   ground is 2.44m (8ft)
   OR
   just bung any bags or jumpers down in two unruly piles at
   each end, then adjust until piles are roughly equidistant*
   and the arguing stops.

   * Ensure at all times that someone keeps an eye on Elaine
   Jenkins because she's always shortening the width of her
   goal when no one's looking.

4. The ball must be spherical, be made of a suitable material, be of a circumference between 68cm and 70cm, weigh between 410g and 450g, and be of a pressure of 0.6–1.1 atmosphere at sea level

OR

belong to Craig Simmons, although he said he might not bring it in today after what happened yesterday lunchtime.

5. A match is played between two teams, each with a maximum of eleven players, one of whom must be the goalkeeper

OR

maybe just wait and see how many turn up, although more than 16-a-side does make the game rather cramped.

When picking teams, remember that Claire Scott is worth at least two players, and that she and Karim Shah are not allowed to play on the same team because that just isn't fair.

6. Each match is controlled by a referee who has full authority to enforce the Laws of the Game in connection with the match

OR

in the event of no referee being available, decisions should be argued about for several minutes until either
a) a resolution is reached,
b) a fight breaks out,
c) or Craig Simmons takes his ball away again.

7. A match lasts for two equal halves of 45 minutes
    OR
    as is more likely, the school bell rings, and the players
    have to go inside for stupid French or Geography.

8. The team that wins the toss of a coin decides which goal
    to attack in the first half or to take the kick-off
    OR
    alternatively, the decision as to which team should take
    the kick-off may simply depend on whose ball is being
    used (please refer to regulation 4, final paragraph).

9. A goal is scored when the whole of the ball passes over
    the goal line, between the posts and under the crossbar,
    provided that no offence has been committed by the team
    scoring the goal
    OR
    in the event of no crossbar being available, the ball must
    not have exceeded the height of the goalkeeper by more
    than the length of a standard 30cm shatterproof ruler.
    Remember, in the event of goal / post disputes, it is
    possible to award ½ a goal.

10. A player is in an offside position if any part of the head,
    body or feet is nearer to the opponents' goal line than
    both the ball and the second-last opponent
    OR
    you may deem it impractical to enforce the offside rule.
    Blatant goal hanging is to be frowned upon, however,

and any player found guilty of such may find themselves the subject of disapproving looks from their classmates for the rest of the day.

11. The team scoring the greater number of goals is the winner. If both teams score no goals or an equal number of goals the match is drawn
OR
given both the high frequency of goals scored, and the number of disputed goal decisions, it may be unclear as to what the final result is. In such circumstances, it is customary for one last round of arguments before afternoon lessons begin, and then for the match to be replayed the following lunchtime, and all future lunchtimes thereafter.

The Last Bee

After the last ee
had uzzed its last uzz,
the irds and the utterflies
did what they could.

 ut soon the field lay are,
few flowers were left,
nature was roken,
and the planet ereft.

401

Steven Camden

Steven Camden aka Polarbear is one of the UK's most acclaimed spoken word artists and storytellers. He has performed all over the world from Manchester to Melbourne and Kuala Lumpur to California, written plays, screenplays and led creative projects all over the place. He has published three YA novels so far along with his recent middle grade debut *My Big Mouth*. His debut poetry collection *Everything All At Once* won the 2019 CLiPPA prize. He has a thing for arctic carnivores.

Prologue

What's it about then?

Well,

It's about the tapestry of moments, woven of a thousand threads.

Different versions of the world swirling inside a thousand heads.

We go from the biggest to the smallest, dropped off, left to fend,

in the secondary school jungle jumbled enemies, new friends.

It's a war zone. It's a haven. It's a stage full of bright lights.

It's a series of scary alleyways walked on a dark night.

Always moving. Unforgiving.

Full of music. Full of living.

Zoom in. One mind. Split screen. Another mind. Another mind.

Another mind. Another mind.

And another mind.

All together. Same place

Same walls. Same space.

Every emotion under the sun. Faith lost. Victories won.

It doesn't stop.

Until the bell. Now it's heaven. Now it's hell.

Who knows? Not me.

I just wrote what I can see.

So what's it about?

Here's my response:

It's about Everything, All At Once.

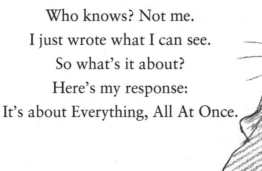

First Day

It looks like a spaceship
a jagged silver spaceship
windows like portals
reflecting the light
no
it looks like the head of
a massive metal monster
its sliding glass mouth
with teeth ready to bite
no
it looks like it sprouted right
out of the floor
ripped through rock, dirt and gravel
burst out of the ground
no
it looks like it fell
from some alien planet
crash-landed on earth
with some terrible sound
no
it looks like
it looks like
I don't know what it looks like
Massive and scary

Noisy
Alive
I feel like a mouse
stepping into the jungle
Tell my mum that I love her
I'm going inside.

Fresh Fish

They give us a map
and our own
private journal
like they think that
we'll never
be heard from
again.
Years from now they'll find
fossils
of scattered Year 7s
buried under the feet
of Years 8
9
and 10.

We sit in assembly
a hall full
of strangers
the cast of a film
where nobody's
the star.
The ground underneath us
completely unstable
as each of us tries
to work out who
we are.

The Head beams a smile
like she's selling us something
welcomes us
into
this family
of school.
Together and separate we look
at each other
scanning for danger
searching for cool.

The bell is much louder
the building's enormous
there's so many people
it's hard to keep track.
Last year we were biggest
now we're the smallest
trying not to slip through
corridor cracks.

We're put into groups
and meet our form tutor
he's dressed like he works
in an office
or bank.
They show us how everything's
on the computer
when asked to choose passwords our minds draw
blank.

We pay for our lunch
with a fingerprint scanner
like the food is some top secret
government plan.
We still have to queue though
same shuffling and chatter and nobody knows
what to do with their hands.

Outside we feel tiny
surrounded by giants
Who just carry on like we're not even there.
It's like we're gazelles in a field full of lions
who've already eaten
so don't really care.

We meet a new teacher
who gives us a book at the end of the lesson
we're all supposed to read.
Some of us groan
as she hands us our copy
some of us hide our excitement
and leave.

Walking along
to the week's final lesson
a few of us laugh when a boy starts
to cry.
Some of us hang back to check
what's the matter
the gap stretches
into a proper divide.

We're supposed to write down
our end-of-week feelings
what we think of our first days of secondary life.
Nobody says anything very revealing
we're basically glad that we're all still alive.

Then the bell goes
and saves us
we look at the people we've chosen to sit with
just as the week ends.
We pack up the journals and maps that they gave us,
'I'll see you on Monday,'
we say to new friends.

Gazelle

Staring out of the window again
the green of the pitches is calling again
feel that itch in my muscles, the sigh in my bones
as the teacher's voice muffles, I drift on my own
breathe in, close my eyes
breathe out and there
outside on the grass, surrounded by air
No talking, no questions, no turn of the screw
just the drum in my heart telling me what to do
so I
run
and I run
and I run and I run
the faster I go
the more I become
I am bullet and arrow
and cheetah
gazelle
I am peregrine falcon and phoenix from hell
I am synapse and fibre and neuron
and flame
I am Thor's hammer lightning, too cosmic to tame
I am me
when I run
I can see
when I run
there is nothing that I cannot be when I run

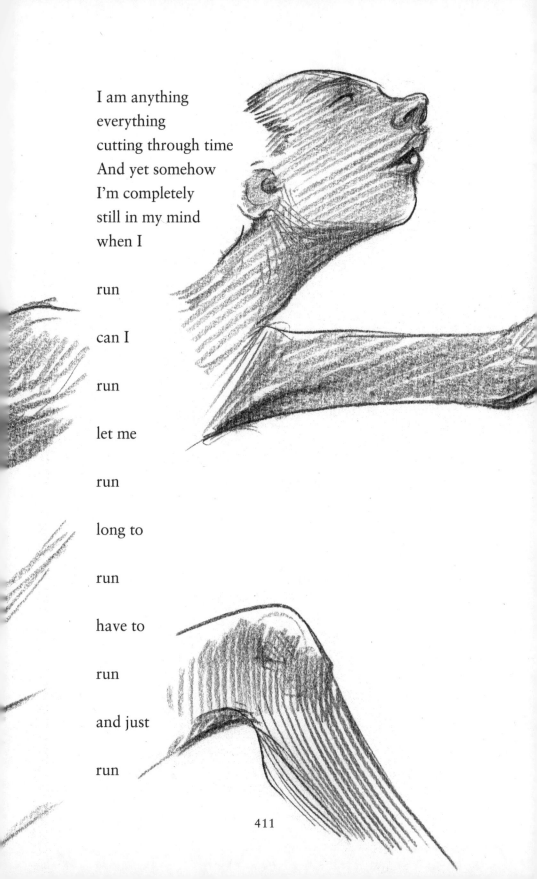

I am anything
everything
cutting through time
And yet somehow
I'm completely
still in my mind
when I

run

can I

run

let me

run

long to

run

have to

run

and just

run

411

and just
run

and just

Constructs

If caring was measured
on
a clock
would midnight be
the most
you could care
or not
caring at all?

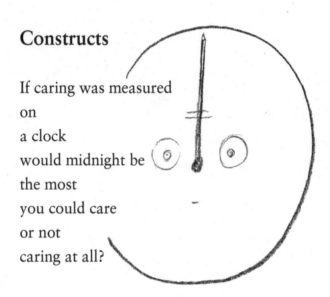

Goal

It was perfect
the timing
like stars aligning or
looking up from your book when the class is silent
just as she does
so perfect you can feel it in your spine
the kind of moment that you know
will be engraved into your mind

Last minute
PE
Josh on the ball
I break free of my marker and give him the call
as I sprint into the box
Josh nutmegs his man
quick look up at me
I'm raising my hand
and he whips it
a perfect curve arcing my way
the keeper comes out
like he's certain to save
but I cut to the near post
spring
off my toes
sun cuts through the clouds like
the universe knows
this is meant to be

the perfect cross from Josh a gift
sent to me
my forehead meets the ball like a perfect piece of destiny
Bang!
Top corner
the ripple in the net
my team mates are all screaming
we won
11–10
I just lie there on the grass
facing up towards the sky
Mr Evans blows his whistle
and I almost start to cry
from pure joy
there's nothing in the world
as good as this
so from the bottom of the pile-on
I just smile
in pure bliss.

Snow

Look at it.
So beautiful.
So perfect.
So pristine.
A hundred fields of perfect snow
So crisp and oh so clean.

So straight along its edges
So smooth on front and back
So many possibilities
Somebody hold me back.

The smell is so
Incredible
The colour blemish free
I want to stroke it like a cat And make it purr for me

I'll build a world
I'll pen a song
I'll fill it with my mind
I'll pour out so much magic stuff
I'll make the pages shine

You either get it
or you don't
So don't bother trying to moan.
This brand-new empty English book
Is mine
So get your own.

415

Chrissie Gittins

Chrissie is an award-winning poet who writes for both children and adults. Three of her five children's poetry collections were selected as Choices for the Children's Poetry Bookshelf and two were shortlisted for the CLiPPA Award. She appeared on BBC's *Countryfile* with *Adder, Bluebell, Lobster* and *Stars in Jars* is a Scottish Poetry Library recommendation. Chrissie won the Belmont Poetry Prize for a single children's poem and was a Manchester Children's Literature Prize finalist. Her poems feature on CBeebies and the Poetry Archive. She has been Writer in Residence in Shetland, with the Refugee Council and Belmarsh Prison. Chrissie has judged the Caterpillar Poetry Prize and is a National Poetry Day Ambassador.

The Little Bottle of Silence

For Sally Crabtree

In my kitchen I have a little bottle of silence.
It's packed full of the gaps
between a duck quacking at her young,

the lull after an alarm goes off,
the hush when the kettle goes off the boil.

Folded over these moments are
the pause between lightning and thunder,
the stillness of a new puddle after a storm,

the calm after the crowd cheers,
the quiet before a firework explodes.

Finally, just under the stopper,
is the tranquillity of a June garden,
the peace of an empty road,

and the long sleep of a new born babe.

Starling

starlings swirl
      starlings chuckle
starlings bicker
and starlings d
          a
            z
              zle

                starlings click
                    starlings trill
                        starlings soar
                and starlings razzle

                    starlings whirr
              starlings bustle
          starlings flock
and starlings sh
            uff
              le

                starlings hurry
                    starlings scream
          starlings whoosh
and starlings s
            qua
              b
                ble

starlings swoop
      starlings chatter
starlings swarm
and they
      cloud the sky with the most
          amazing
              murmurations

The Powder Monkey

This is the moment I dread,
my eyes sting with smoke,
my ears sing with cannon fire.
I see the terror rise inside me,
coil a rope in my belly to keep it down.
I chant inside my head to freeze my nerve.

Main mast, mizzen mast, foremast,
belfry, capstan, waist.

We must keep the fire coming.
If I dodge the sparks
my cartridge will be safe,
if I learn my lessons
I can be a seaman,
if I close my eyes to eat my biscuit
I will not see the weevils.

Main mast, mizzen mast, foremast,
shot lockers, bowsprit, gripe.

Don't stop to put out that fire,
run to the hold,
we must fire at them
or they will fire at us.

Main mast, mizzen mast, foremast,
belfry, capstan, waist.

My mother never knew me,
but she would want to know this –
I can keep a cannon going,
I do not need her kiss.

Before 1794 children aged six upward went to sea.
After 1794 the minimum age was thirteen.

Government Health Warning

Don't squash peas on your knees,
Don't grate carrot on a parrot,
Don't tangle pears in your nostril hairs,
Never risk a quid on a squid.

Don't pour bottled beer in your ear,
Never slice apple pies on your thighs.
Never wash your pullovers with yesterday's leftovers.
Don't entice a bowl of egg fried rice.

Don't assume that tarragon's a paragon,
Or try to run faster than a bag of spinach pasta,
Don't try a lunge at Victoria sponge,
A cake with a steak is a mistake.

Bravado never works with avocado,
A flickin's not the thing to give to chicken,
Don't go and stutter on the b-b-b-b-butter,
Never feed mice on ice.

Careful not to ravage a coy savoy cabbage,
Never have a tussle with a mussel,
Don't ever hurry with a spicy prawn curry,
Don't boast about your buttered toast.

Don't pour jelly in your welly,
Don't dribble tagliatelle on your older brother's belly.
Never do the tango with a ripe and juicy mango,
If you do then you're sure to pay the price!

DO NOT FEED THE MICE

421

Three

My best friend *has* a best friend,
she is a bester friend than me,
but when they have a falling out
my friend is best with me.

The Pencil Stub

For William Penn School, Stoke Newington

When I was new I drew
the leather shoe lace on a magic shoe.

You shaved me down.

I wound my lead around
the leaves of an ancient
willow tree.

You shaved me down.

I drew a circle, you
rubbed me out,
I became a careful square.

You shaved me down.

I was happiest tracing
the face of your mother –
her plaited hair,
her sparkling slate grey eyes.

And still you shaved me down.

I could still conjure the universe,
skirt Saturn with a silver ring,
chase the rain falling from
a shooting star.

423

Twelve Moons

JANUARY – Cold Moon.
Winter's younger brother,
Sun has not strength to thaw.

FEBRUARY – Snow Moon, Sleet Moon.
When the spruce tips fall,
When trees crack because of the cold.

MARCH – Worm Moon, Sap Moon, Little Spring Moon.
When the leaves break forth,
Worms raise their heads.

APRIL – Pink Moon, Big Spring Moon.
Budding time for apple blossom, cherry blossom,
    tulips.

MAY – Flower Moon, Planting Moon, Frog Moon.
Moon of waiting,
Moon of green leaves.

JUNE – Strawberry Moon, Rose Moon.
Full Leaf Moon,
Berries Ripen Moon.

JULY – Thunder Moon, Raspberry Moon, Hot Moon.
Little harvest,
Moon of the young corn.

AUGUST – Grain Moon, Plum Moon, Summer Moon.
Moon of joyful, Moon of the ripening,
Moon young ducks begin to fly.

SEPTEMBER – Harvest Moon, Nut Moon, Snow Goose
    Moon.
Moon of the brown leaves,
Moon when the deer paw the earth.

OCTOBER – Hunter's Moon, Blood Moon, Wilted Moon.
Moon when the wind shakes off the leaves,
Freeze begins at stream edge.

NOVEMBER – Frost Moon, Deer Rutting Moon, Long
    Moon.
Heading to Winter Moon,
Much white frost on grass.

DECEMBER – Long Night Moon, Evergreen Moon,
    Eccentric Moon.
Sun has travelled home to rest,
Moon when the deer shed their antlers,
Moon of Respect.

Native Americans give names to each of the full moons
to keep track of the passing year. This poem brings
together some of the names which the tribes use.

Gerard Benson

Gerard Benson was an actor, poet, story-teller, book reviewer, editor and co-founder of the Poems on the Undergound project, Barrow poet and former teacher at the Central School of Speech and Drama. He published ten volumes and poetry and prize-winning collections for children. He lived in Bradford with his wife Cathy, and he was appointed the city's first poet laureate.

A Small Star

I live on a small star
Which it is my job to look after;
It whirls through space
Wrapped in a cloak of water

It is a wonderful star:
Wherever you look there is life,
Though it's held at either end
In a white fist of ice.

There are creatures that move
Through air, sea and earth,
And growing things everywhere
Make beauty from dirt.

Everything is alive!
Even the very stones:
Amazing crystals grow
Deep under the ground.

And all the things belong,
Each one to the other.
I live on a precious star
Which it is my job to look after.

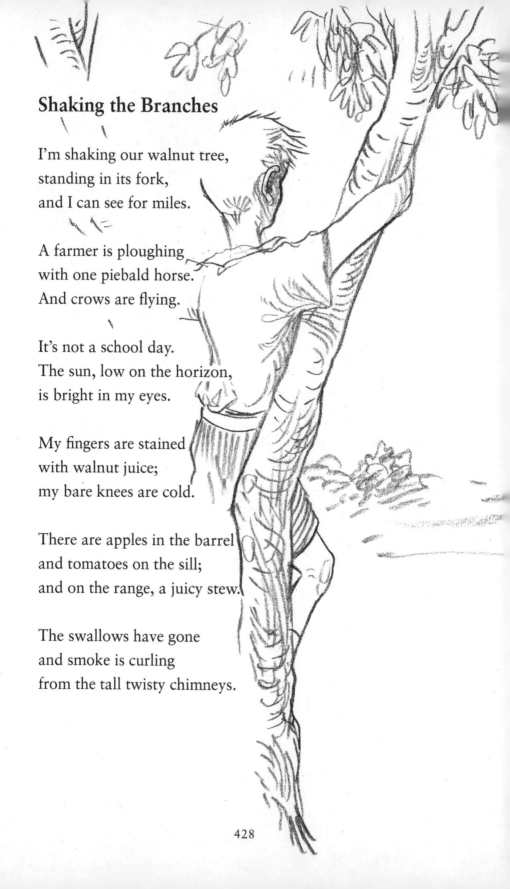

Shaking the Branches

I'm shaking our walnut tree,
standing in its fork,
and I can see for miles.

A farmer is ploughing
with one piebald horse.
And crows are flying.

It's not a school day.
The sun, low on the horizon,
is bright in my eyes.

My fingers are stained
with walnut juice;
my bare knees are cold.

There are apples in the barrel
and tomatoes on the sill;
and on the range, a juicy stew.

The swallows have gone
and smoke is curling
from the tall twisty chimneys.

My parents are a hundred miles away
in a bombed city.
Churchill is on the news,

and I am standing in the fork
of a walnut tree
shaking the branches.

Spring Assembly

Right! As you all know,
It's spring pretty soon
And I want a real good one this year.
I want no slackers, I want SPRING!
That's S-P-R-I-N-G! Got it?
Spring! Jump! Leap!
Energy! Busting out all over!
Nothing so beautiful! Ding-a-ding-a-ding!

Flowers: I want a grand show from you –
Lots of colour, of loveliness.
Daffodils: blow those gold trumpets.
Crocuses: poke up all over the parks and gardens,
Yellows, purples, whites; paint that picture.
And a nice show of blossom on the fruit trees
Make it look like snow, just for a laugh,
Or loads of pink candy floss.

Winds: blow things about a bit.
North, South, East, West, get it all stirred up.
Get March nice and airy and exciting.

Rain: lots of shimmering showers please.
Soak the earth after its winter rest.
Water those seeds and seedlings.
And seeds: start pushing up.
Up! Up! Up! Let's see plenty of green.

Sunshine! give the earth a sparkle
After the rain. Warm things up.

And you birds: I haven't forgotten you.
Fill the gardens with your song.
Build your nests (you'll remember how).
And you lambs: set an example,
Jump, leap, bound, bounce, spring!

And kids: ditch those coats and scarves,
And get running and skipping.
Use that playground, none of this
Hanging about by the school wall
With your hands in your jeans pockets.
It's spring, I tell you.
And you're part of it
And we've got to have a real good one this year.

Duffy

The white cat furies
In a squirm of purring.

He writhes in his delight,
Rolling his restless head
He tunnels my ready lap.

He loops his length
Hooping his lithe spine.

The white cat settles,
Licks at a stiffened leg,
Then sleeps – a lazy shape.

The white cat dreams of snow fields
The small musical pipes of birds,
Licking his lips in sleep.

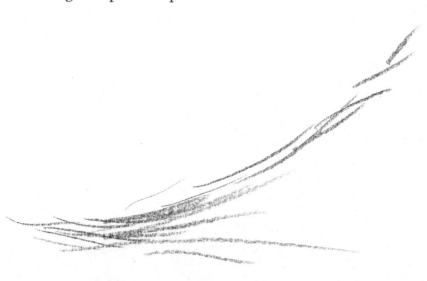

Fishing

There is a fine
line

between fishing
and standing
on the bank
like
an idiot.

Wet Playtime

(Dave's version)

Mr Finn
Lets us stay in;
Mrs Grout
Makes us go out.

(Matt's version)

Mr Finn
Makes us stay in;
Mrs Grout
Lets us go out.

433

A Tale of Two Citizens

I have a Russian friend who lives in Minsk
And wears a lofty hat of beaver's skinsk
(which does not suit a man so tall and thinsk).
He has a frizzly beard upon his chinsk.
He keeps his britches up with safety pinsk.
'They're so much better than those thingsk
Called belts and braces don't you thinksk?'
You'll hear him say, the man from Minsk.

He has a Polish pal who's from Gdansk.
Who lives by selling drinksks to football fansk,
And cheese rolls, from a little caravansk.
(He finds it pleasanter than robbing banksk.)
He also uses pinsk to hold up his pantsk.
'Keep up one's pantsk with rubber bandsk!?
It can't be donesk! It simply cant'sk!
Not in Gdansk!' he'll say. 'No thanksk!'

They're so alike that strangers often thinksk
That they are brothers, yesk, or even twinsk.
'I live in Minsk but I was born in Omsk,'
Says one. His friend replies, 'That's where I'm fromsk!
Perhapsk we're brothers after all, not friendsk.'
So they wrote homesk and asked their Mumsk
But found they weren'tsk; so they shook handsk
And left for Minsk, and for Gdansk.

Martin Glynn

Martin is a lecturer in criminology at Birmingham City University and a poet, children's author, and storyteller, with over forty years of experience working in schools, libraries, and communities. As a father, grandfather, and great grandfather, Martin sees poetry as a way of communicating across the generations, as well as keeping the oral tradition alive.

Poetry is . . .

Take a
P . . . O . . . E . . .T . . . R 'n' Y
Pencil 'n' paper
Da wurdz will fly
Like spittin from yer mouth
Aim inna direcshun
Movin inna circle
Jus' like convecshun
Yer can't critisize
Da size ofa poem
Sum 'r' dull
Otherz 'r' glowin
Wurdz transfushan
A sentence injecshun
'U' can't stop
A poemz infecshun
Rap ... rhyme ... rhythm ... beat
Short ... fat ... thin
No idea ... can't begin
Puttin' brain power
To da test
Once you've started
'U' can't rest
Whisper ... scream it .. shout it .. sing
Yer wurdz express .. anyting
Da wurdz to a beat
Or no strucha

Once 'U' start
Da poemz gotcha
Can't escape
From wot itz sayin
Poetry knowz
Da game yer playin'
Da flow …. goez slow
Sumtimez last
Sumtimez lingers
Dusunt last
Short … fat … long .. thin .. funny 'n' serious
Painful .. emoshunal … soothin' 'n' delirious
Inspirashun .. perspirashun
Workin' on a poem is pure frustrashun
Style … form … length … subject matta
Jus' like a fish
'U' will batta
Da life out ofa sentence
Strangle da syllable
Choke da verb
Da feelingz unbearable
1st draft … 2nd draft
Then 'U' edit
Smile on yer face
Then take credit
Yer read it back
Yer eyes start glowin
When yer realize
Yer've just created a POEM

At Dis School

Firs' day bak at skool .. don't feel cool ... bullies rule ...
Heart pumpin' .. racin' ... jumpin' ..... thumpin'
Frightenin' ... like lightenin ... .. bouncin' ... from
One spot to annuva ... ain't gotta sista or a bruvva
At dis skool ....
Feel da feer growin' .. hope I'm not showin' .. feer
Breathin' hard .. I'm blowin' ... I'm nervus ...
I'm worried ... coz I'm alone .. on my own ...
Ain't feelin' cool ... in da playground .. bad kids rule
At dis skool ....
Pepul kickin' ball ... playin' marbles ... conkers .... Jostlin'
Fightin' ... actin' bonkers ...... da gazin' eyez .. I realize ...
I want dis moment ter end ... don't want ter spend
Any more time ... frettin' ... I'm gettin' anxious ... I really
Want dis moment .. ter end .. where is he .. where is he
There he is ... my best friend .. at dis skool
I ain't no trend setter .. I ain't no blinger ... I ain't got
A Gameboy .. 'n' I ain't no good singa ... not bad at
Computers ... not too bad at gym ... don't have slick
Trainers ... know how ter swim ... but one ting I have ..
It ain't no lates' trend ... I've got sumting more ..
I have bes' friend .. at dis skool ...

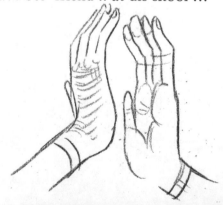

Ranting

I ain't got an illness, ain't gotta disease
I jus' wanna sandwich with mature cheddar cheese
I'm not an alien from space or a dog with nuff fleas
I jus' wanna sandwich with mature cheddar cheese
Don't need a degree of other expertise
Coz I jus' wanna sandwich with mature cheddar cheese
I ask 'n' say 'thankyou' 'n' always say 'please'
Coz all I want is a sandwich with mature cheddar cheese
This anguish 'n' frustration nearly brings me ter my knees
Wen I can't get a sandwich with mature cheddar cheese
'No I don't want other fillings,' I say with calm ease
I jus' wanna sandwich with mature cheddar cheese
I remain calm, deep breathe, think it's some form of tease
Coz I jus' wanna sandwich with mature cheddar cheese
I stare at the shop assistant, face full of unease
'N' say *'I jus' wanna sandwich with mature cheddar cheese'*
I start gettin' angry, I clench my hand 'n' squeeze
Coz I jus' wanna sandwich with mature cheddar cheese
Do I have ter climb a mountain or chop down some trees
Wen all I want is a sandwich with mature cheddar cheese
Do you want me ter move to a town overseas?
Ter get me a sandwich with mature cheddar cheese
I went home, took some bread, 'n' as smooth as a breeze
I made my own sandwich with mature cheddar cheese

Breaking Free

Time to make a difference, 'N'
Time to walk tall, 'N'
Time to do some healing, 'N'
Time to break the fallin', 'N'
Time to talk to loved ones, 'N'
Time to stop the talk 'N'
Time to be at peace 'N'
Time to walk the walk 'N'
Time to take some action 'N'
Time to move ahead 'N'
Time to do the journey 'N'
Time to rest my head 'N'
Time to take a moment 'N'
Time to be me,
The time has arrived 'N'

It's time to break free

Luv Beat

I'm the ackee, you're the saltfish
I'm the rice 'n' you're the peas
I'm the bank 'n' you're the river
I'm the bun 'n' you're the cheese

I'm the ying 'n' you're the yang
I'm the tai 'n' you're the chi
I'm the biscuit .... you're the sugar
I'm the water ... you're the tea

I'm the sock 'n' you're the foot
I'm the toes 'n' you're the shoe
I'm the eyes 'n' you're the glasses
I'm the old 'n' you're the new

I'm the bottom ... you're the top
I'm the north ... you're the south
I'm the spirit .. you're the soul
I'm the tongue 'n' you're the mouth

I'm the rhythm ... you're the beat
I'm the chorus .. you're the song
I'm the melody ... you're the bridge
I'm the weak .. 'n' you're the strong

I'm the tree 'n' you're the forest
I'm the petal .. you're the flowa

I'm the daylight .. you're the moonshine
I'm the minute you're the hour

I'm the teeth 'n' you're the toothpaste
I'm the soap 'n' you're the skin
I'm the water .. you're the shower
I'm the needle .. you're the pin

I'm the ship .. 'n' you're the anchor
I'm the rain 'n' you're the breeze
I'm the lemon you're the … ade
I'm the chill 'n' you're the freeze

I'm the blood .. you're the heartbeat
I'm the muscles .. you're the veins
I'm the breath 'n' you're the lungs
I'm the thought 'n' you're the brain

I'm a half 'n' you're the other half
I'm the fingers .. you're the glove
I'm the silver .. you're the gold
I'm below …. 'n' you're above

I'm the ache 'n' you're the ointment
I'm the massage 'n' you're the aching feet
I'm the movement .. you're the stillness
I'm the bassline 'n' you're the beat.

Love beat

Rain

As I look back 'n' reflect how far that I've come
In my journey in life 'n' how it begun
Thru' the ups 'n' the downs ... Thru the highs 'n' the lows
The lessons I've learned 'n' how that I've grown

There's one journey left, cannot fake, cannot run
It's the passin' of knowledge from a father 2 his son
2 leave him with the tools ... 2 create a life plan
'N' how 2 make a transition from a boy to a man

But what can I say that will help him along
2 understand the difference between rite 'n' wrong
I'd say 'U' have a proud heritage .. from a powerful race
Know who you are 'n' what is your place

It's about havin' values 'n' havin' good health
Understandin' your history 'n' knowledge of self
It's about independence 'n' not turnin' mad
Knowin' I am your friend as well as your Dad

It's about being smart with a developin' mind
Knowin' at times I will have 2 be cruel 2 be kind
Settin' clear goals 'n' a pathway in life
'N' respectin' all women be it sister or wife

Use knowledge ... be honest ... take pride in your skin
Givin' up ain't an option if you wanna win
Celebrate your skin tone .... the shape of your nose
The texture of your hair 'n' how yer soul grows

Don't do as I do, you must find ya own way
My role as your Dad is to guide not just say
Love all that you are …. be all you can be
Learn nothing in life ever comes free

Sacrifice 'n' success 'n' doin' yer best
Knowin' when ter say no! 'n' when you must rest
Be a respectable person know when ter butt out
Don't act like a gangster or live with self-doubt

Respect all yer elders …. don't fear the word fail
Or sell out yer culture or put it on sale
Have morals 'n' values as part of your plan
'N' you'll make the transition from boy to a man

So as I look back 'n' reflect how far that I've come
In my journey in life 'n' how it begun
Thru' the ups 'n' the downs … Thru the highs 'n' the lows
The lessons I've learned 'n' how that I've grown

There's one journey left, cannot fake, cannot run
It's the passin' of knowledge from a father 2 his son
2 leave him with the tools … 2 create a life plan
'N' how 2 make a transition from a boy to a man

One final thought always reach for the sky
And men aren't men if they say they can't cry

Thanks Mum

At times when I am lonely
'N' I have lost my way
Can't see through the darkness
'N' I don't know what to say

Like a new child I cannot walk
I fall on shaky ground
Then you pick me up again
I get lost 'N' then found

My heart is sometimes tired
It's hard to carry on
Like a breeze, you cool me down
Then my fears have gone

You hold me tight, 'N' squeeze me hard
No longer feeling low 'N' cold
Your gentle touch, your loving ways
Your love jus' makes me whole

A lesson learned, some wisdom gained
You repaired my broken wings
Where darkness ruled the light now shines
It's love and warmth you bring

Without you sitting close to me
I don't feel complete
You truly are amazing
Perfect and unique

Thanks Mum

A. F. Harrold

A. F. Harrold is a poet, performer, beard-wearer and author who has written many different sorts of things. As well as poems (in books like *The Book of Not Entirely Useful Advice*, with Mini Grey) he's written funny stories, such as the Fizzlebert Stump and Greta Zargo series, and strange illustrated novels like *The Imaginary* (with Emily Gravett) and *The Song from Somewhere Else* (with Levi Pinfold). He has put together some poetry anthologies (like *Midnight Feasts*) and can often be found in schools, running poetry workshops and talking about being A. F. Harrold. But he's always at his happiest when he's simply allowed out on stage to perform poems and generally be silly with words for money. He lives in Reading and has two cats.

Blackbirds and Bananas

A banana is yellow, with little bits of black.
A blackbird is black, with little bits of yellow.

A banana grows up in a tree.
A blackbird grows up in a tree.

A banana is about the size of a blackbird.
A blackbird is about the size of a banana.

A banana is a surprising, but not unheard of, pie filling.
A blackbird is a surprising, but not unheard of, pie filling.

A banana. A blackbird.
A blackbird. A banana.

Listen!
My lunchbox is singing.

The Point

Point to the sky.
Draw a line from your finger.
It'll go on forever.
Through light and through darkness.
Past astronauts sleeping.
Past clouds and past planets.
Through silence unmeasured.
Through time uncounted.
A line that's so long.
It will never stop going.
Long after you've dropped
your hand to your side.
And gone back indoors.
That line is still sketching.
Onwards and outwards.
Universe threading.
Oh, your finger's a marvel.
Take care where you point it.

Postcards From The Hedgehog

i.

Dear Mum,

Beautiful weather.
I saw a fox last night,
did as you always said
and rolled into a ball.
After a while it went away.
I was a bit scared all the same.
Wish you were here,

love Simon.

ii.

Dear Mum,

Lovely weather today.
Just saw a really pretty girl.
Not sure how to approach her.
She makes me really shy
but just all warm inside.
I rolled up into a ball.
Wish you were here,

love Simon.

iii.

Dear Mum,

It's raining today. I ate a slug.
Wasn't as good as the ones
you used to give us.
Tomorrow I think I'll approach the girl.
Perhaps I'll take her a slug.
She makes me ever so nervous.
I rolled up into a ball.
Wish you were here,

love Simon.

iv.

Dear Mum,

Sun's come out again.
This morning I was very brave
and I went to see her.
I edged up very carefully as you suggested,
but when I spoke to her
I discovered she was actually a pine-cone.
I felt very embarrassed.
Rolled up into a ball.
Wish you were here,

love Simon.

451

Between the Covers

I sit soft on the sofa
with snow whipping my eyes,
with chill rock against my cheek.

Wolves howl,
but their tiny voices
vanish in the storm.

I need shelter,
to get under cover,
find a cave.

My cloak so thin,
my boots full of slush,
my eyes sting and my cheeks crackle.

I get up,
make a cup of tea,
look out the kitchen window at the summer.

A blackbird hops on the fence,
eying worms,
singing his snatch of sunlit song,

and then –
back to the sofa,
back to the mountain,
back to the winter,
back to the book.

Troll Song

'It wasn't always my ambition to live under a bridge.
There came a point though where a decision had to be made.

It was either here or in a swamp or in a cave.

On the plus side, there's cold running water all the time.
On the minus side, I am living under a bridge.
There's little privacy and less in the way of respect.

It's only a small bridge. My feet stick out when I sleep.
I bang my head more than I'd like.
I get into arguments with ducks.

People look down on me, living under a bridge.
But it's a tradition, my mum said, and tradition's tradition.
Sometimes I eat the ducks. Those are arguments I've won.

On either river bank are pastures. Lush-lands.
I like the smell in spring of the hundred different flowers.
I never mention this when other trolls come to visit.

I read a lot of books. They contain other worlds.
For a time I can imagine I'm not living under a bridge.
You can learn things in books too, important useful things:
I eat every goat I see these days, just to be on the safe side.'

Autumn Speaks to the Leaves

'Won't you *please* get off the trees?!'

Parasol (Just a Light Shower)

Light falls
like rain from the sky.

It pools in puddles,
glowing discs on the pavement – -

passers-by are lit from below,
faces ripe for telling ghost stories.

Kids run open mouthed, heads back,
catching light on their tongues –

spitting glowing globules
at one another across the playground.

Dogs shake brilliance
from their blazing bright fur.

Cats lurk sullen,
eyes flashing in the glistering undergrowth.

After the rain
trees drip dazzling diamonds.

Parasols are folded up,
put back in their racks until the next light shower.

David Orme

David Orme has written over 250 books on many different subjects, from astronomy to keeping fit, and graphic novels about a superhero called Boffin Boy. The work he likes best, though, involves poetry: writing poems, editing anthologies, and writing books for teachers with ideas on teaching poetry. He has visited many schools, reading and talking about poetry, and encouraging everyone to have a go.

Guess the title!

A

Hot

Day in

Egypt. The

Pharoah said, 'I

Won't be buried in a hole

In the ground! Build me something

Really, really, special! So they did. And it

Was absolutely enormous! The Pharoah loved it!

But then he said 'Whatever are we going to call this thing?'

July 20th, 1969: What they didn't find on the Moon

'The Moon isn't made of cheese.
It's nothing but rocks and dust,
Just like the Earth.
A pity really,
For I had brought my bread and butter
And was looking forward to a sandwich.

'There isn't a Man in the Moon.
There's no one here at all.
A pity really, for I had made up a moon language,
And was looking forward to a chat.

'There's nothing here at all.
I'm so disappointed,
I've decided to come home.'

And as the Moon lander
Flashed upwards,
The Man in the Moon
Swept aside the dust,
Broke off a piece of really ripe cheese,
Munched it,
Licked his huge hairy lips,
And waved the Earthman
Goodbye.

Football in the Rain

It's drizzling.
'Football practice!'
'Oh, sir!
Do we have to?'
We look hopefully at Mr Tomkins,
But he says,
'Don't be such babies!'
So out we go.

It's raining harder.
We all start to moan,
'Can't we go in, sir?
We're getting soaked!'
But Mr Tomkins is not impressed.
'Tough. Get on with it!'
He says, putting up his umbrella
And retreating to the touchline.

It's coming down in buckets.
There are puddles all over the pitch,
And the rest is just mud.
Eddy falls over,
And comes up looking like
The Mud Monster from Hell.
We all start falling over,
Because we all want to look like that.

It's really chucking it down.
Mr Tomkins gets rain in his whistle.
gurgle-gurgle-PHEEEP!
'Everybody in!'
We start moaning again.
'Oh, sir!
Do we have to?'

Tyrannosaurus Chicken

They say
I'm just a chicken.

They use my name
for cowards:

'You're chicken!'
They shout.

But I've just found out
Something really exciting.

The chicken on the next perch
Said, 'Guess what!

WE ARE DESCENDED FROM DINOSAURS!'

I'm looking forward to when
The man who collects the eggs comes round.

We've got it all planned.
He's going to get

The biggest shock
Of his life!

461

Home time at half past three

It's a tough mission,
Getting home:
First problem,
A red sea of buses;
Mr Lollipop divides it with his staff,
But will we make it across?
The drivers are
(Cross that is),
They call up dragons
On their mobile phones,
And tell them they're going to be late.
But we're through,
Past lamp posts that bend down
And pinch your chips when you're not looking,
And pillar boxes with dark eyes under their helmets.
Mums are steering armoured cars
With dangerous nippers inside.
Don't forget now,
Watch out for lifting manhole covers
With green snouts under them;
SOMEONE
Flushed a crocodile
Down the toilet.

Beware werewolves
Lurking in their warehouses,
And gingerbread cars
With smiling faces.

It's a tough mission,
Getting home;
It's a scary world out there,
But . . .
We made it!

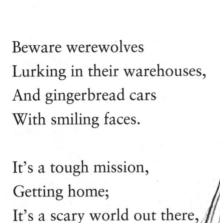

Beside the Sea-Side

Oh I *do* like to be beside the sea-side,
I do like to be beside the sea:
I do like to walk along the sewage pipe
Where the sand's got lumps
And the air smells ripe
I do wish the sea would give the beach a wipe
Beside the sea-side,
Beside the sea.

Oh I *do* like to walk beside the sea-side,
I do like to walk beside the sea,
I do like to see just what the tide's brought in
A plastic bag or two, a rusty tin,
A long dead fish with a ghastly grin
Beside the sea-side,
Beside the sea.

Oh I *do* like to paddle by the sea-side,
I do like to paddle in the sea,
The sea's so dirty now that no one knows
What is oozing stickily around your toes
You'll have a lovely time if you hold your nose
Beside the sea-side
Beside the sea.

Don't Feed the Yeti

Never leave food for the yeti,
He really must hunt for his own,
Once he gets a taste for spaghetti,
He'll never leave us alone.
He'll be snuffling round at the cat flap,
He'll be there when we open the door,
He'll come wandering into the kitchen
Leaving footprints all over the floor.
He'll be sitting and watching the telly,
He'll sprawl all over the chairs,
When it comes to refinement and manners,
He's worse than a grizzly bear.
Yetis are really wild creatures,
From the snowiest parts of Tibet,
They eat nothing but snow-flavoured ice-cream
(It's the only food they can get).
So don't give him cold mashed potatoes,
or toad in the hole; you will find
If you're plagued by the neighbourhood yeti
You have to be cruel to be kind!

Shauna Darling Robertson

Shauna Darling Robertson grew up in the north-east of England and now lives in the south-west. Her poems for adults and children have been performed by actors, displayed on buses, used as song lyrics, turned into short films and repurposed as comic art. You'll also find them in lots of books, including anthologies such as *A Poem for Every Day of the Year*, *Shaping the World*, *Wonder: The Natural History Museum Poetry Book*, *Poems for 7 Year Olds* and *Poems for 8 Year Olds*. In Shauna's first collection for children, *Saturdays at the Imaginarium*, she delves into the awesomeness of the human imagination and creates worlds where birds can't fly but thoughts can, a kid catches dreams in a net, and the weather forecast predicts an ear-to-ear grin nearly two miles high. Her second, *You Are Not Alone* adult readers, and explores diverse experiences of mental health and wellbeing.

The Followers

ep
heep
heep sheep
P

    heep sheep sheep
    p sheep sheep sheep sheep
    ep sheep sheep sheep
    eep

            sheep sheep sheep sheep
                sheep sheep sheep sheep sheep
       sheep sheep sheep sheep
  sheep sheep

            sheep
   sheep sheep sheep sheep sheep
   sheep sheep sheep sheep sheep sheep sheep
           sheep sheep sheep sheep sheep
        sheep sheep
        sheep she
      sheep sheep sheep she
        sheep sheep sh
           s

Earthtalk

The sea has a story to tell us
      if only we'd wait on the beach.

And I wish we'd just sit here and listen
      to all that the wind has to teach.

The earth will share mountains of wisdom
      as soon as we grasp more than speech.

The trees gently whisper their secrets
      and offer up knowledge for free.

The birds chatter openly to us –
      whatever seems locked, there's a key.

The whole world, it talks to us daily.
      Can't anyone hear it but me?

The Poetry Guerrilla

That morning
the world woke up
to poetry.

Like some kind of Santa Claus of words
the poetry guerrilla had laboured all night
spreading the pleasure of line and verse.

At breakfast, the shell from Bettina's boiled egg
unravelled to reveal a ballad.

At the launderette, Susie pulled three pairs of pantoums
from the drier. A little wiggle and they were a perfect fit.

Uncle Jim found a limerick printed on his lottery ticket.
His numbers didn't win, but still, he had a giggle.

Alice the hairdresser's headache was instantly fixed
by a haiku etched into an aspirin.

Reverend Crick, the vicar, found his vestry filled with villanelles
which served as his sermons for the next six months.

When Tammy ordered take-out she got
a triolet with her chicken tikka, spare ribs with a sestina
and a free side order of odes.

But wait – someone had broken into the bank!
(Turns out they took nothing, just deposited sixty sonnets
and a cento.)

Order! cried Captain Collis, as he sought to calm the crowd
with a warning shot from his hilltop cannon.
But it fired cantos, not cannonballs,
littering the town with a lengthy, living legend.

Brushing my teeth at bedtime, I noticed
a fading clerihew finger-written on the foggy bathroom window.
It had my name on it
and as I looked up I swear I saw
a shadowy figure heading for the horizon.
Man? Woman? Child?
I couldn't say, but this I know –

there was a spring in their step,
a glint in their eye
and so much language on their lips.

Things People Have Told Me In The Past Few Weeks

You need a strong core to excel at rock climbing.
If I go to Edinburgh, I'll have a blast.
We can be short-sighted and long-sighted, both at the same
    time.
As an actor, Michael Cera has often been typecast.
        Most of our communications have moved online.

There are so many things that need to be assessed
when you're choosing a new wheelchair.
In English, there are more than forty ways to say 'yes'.
I really ought to listen to Lily Allen's *Not Fair*.
        Young people suffer from higher rates of loneliness.

My new blue shirt looks really great.
In Yiddish, a grumbly person is called a kvetch.
The West has let down Afghanistan in so many ways.
Bolivia's top two languages are Spanish and Quechua.
        Most people don't really know what to say.

When people feel seen and heard, given the time of day,
they're far more likely to rise, to shine.
The first writing media were tablets made of clay.
Here's a conversation starter: 'I feel lonely sometimes.
        Do you ever feel that way?'

A Matter of [   ]

[Sub-Saharan Africa / Time / Wednesday] is a great healer.
I haven't got [underwear / surfaces / time].
It'll be different next [time / door / wardrobe].

It's about [three / a boy / time].
We're running out of [time / vacuums / musical instruments].
We have all the [car parks / time / ideas] in the world.

[Compost / time / the moon] is on our side.
There's a [time / field / weather] for everything.
This is my [fence / teddy bear / time].

What [time / river / drink] do you call this?
It's high [five / time / tide] you did something about the situation.
I've told you a hundred [lies / hairstyles / times].

I'd love to travel back in [trousers / time / custard].
I need more [time / tingle / test results].
Only [hosepipes / smiles / time] will tell.

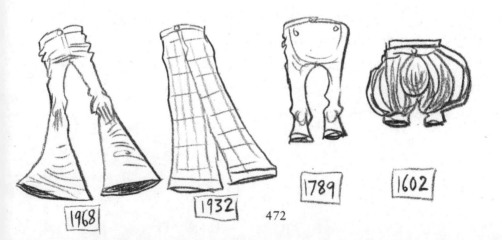

1968   1932   1789   1602

One Whole Minute

So this morning when I was getting ready,
instead of ruminating and cogitating,
I spent one whole minute
feeling the shower's hot rain
pitter-pattering in mini rivers over my shoulders.

When I left the house to get the bus,
instead of cogitating and deliberating,
for one whole minute I listened
to the city rumbling and hissing
and going about its business.

At lunchtime in the canteen,
instead of deliberating and mulling and brooding,
I stood in the queue and for one whole minute, sniffed and
    smelled
till I knew exactly what was on the menu
and what I felt like tasting today.

On the bus back,
instead of mulling and brooding and chewing over,
I sat beside Hayley and for one whole minute
gave her my total, unbroken attention
while she went on and on about Justin again.

Then tonight, while you were all watching TV,
instead of chewing over and ruminating,

I sat for one whole minute and watched each of you, watching
and your eyes, your faces were priceless,
how they moved between tiny frowns and little smiles.

Art Therapy

Show me the colour of your fury, she said
and pushed a box of chalks across the table.

Eyes blazing, I snatched the box
and emptied the whole idiotic lot
right into her cream-trousered lap.

A pause. Then she leapt up –
clapped her perfect hands, threw back her head
and laughed and laughed.

Brilliant! Vivid! A psychedelic riot! she hooted,
whirling around in chalk-dust circles, arms outstretched,
eyes twinkling with mischief.

In that instant I twigged
that she'd probably once been
exactly in my position

and I felt sorry about the trousers
but also not sorry at all

and I tried really hard to stay true to my filthy mood
but the hooting and the whirling got hold of me too

till there we were, the pair of us
spinning and twisting and whooping and howling,
thinking, *who knew*
these were the colours of our fury.

John Foster

John Foster was born in 1941 and grew up in a village called Scotby, near Carlisle. After university, he became an English teacher and taught for twenty years before becoming a full-time writer. While he was teaching, he wrote school textbooks and in 1979 compiled his first poetry anthology. He has now had over one hundred poetry anthologies published and eleven books of his own poetry. The most popular anthology is *The Poetry Chest*, and the most popular collection of his own poems is *Four O'Clock Friday*.

He writes poems because he loves words – his favourite word is hullabaloo – and in poems you can play with words.

He lives in a village called Standlake, in Oxfordshire.

My Baby Brother's Secrets

When my baby brother
wants to tell me a secret,
he comes right up close.
But instead of putting his lips
against my ear,
he presses his ear
tightly against my ear.
Then, he whispers so softly
that I can't hear
a word he is saying.

My baby brother's secrets
are safe with me.

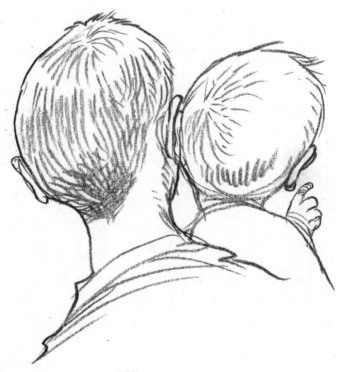

November

November is a grey road
Cloaked in mist.
A twist of wood-smoke
In the gathering gloom.
A scurrying squirrel
Hoarding acorns.
A steel-grey river
Glinting in the twilight.
A grey rope
Knotted around a threadbare tree.

Four O'Clock Friday

Four o'clock Friday, I'm home at last,
Time to forget the week that's past.
On Monday, in break they stole my ball
And threw it over the playground wall.
On Tuesday afternoon, in games
They threw mud at me and called me names.
On Wednesday, they trampled my books on the floor,
So Miss kept me in because I swore.
On Thursday, they laughed after the test
'Cause my marks were lower than the rest.
Four o'clock Friday, at last I'm free,
For two whole days they can't get at me.

Dad's Hiding in the Shed

Dad's hiding in the shed.
He's made me swear
Not to tell Mum
That he's hiding in there.

She was having a lie-down
With the curtains drawn.
We were playing cricket
Out on the lawn.

The scores were level.
It was really tense.
Dad had just hit a six
Right over the fence.

I bowled the next ball
As fast as I could.
Dad tried it again
As I knew he would.

But he missed and the ball
Struck him hard on the toe.
He cried out in pain
And, as he did so,

He let go of the bat.
It flew up in an arc
And crashed through the window
Where Mum lay in the dark.

Dad's hiding in the shed.
He's made me swear
Not to tell Mum
That he's hiding in there.

Spells

I crackle and spit. I lick and leap higher.
This is the spell of the raging fire.

I clasp and I grasp. I grip in a vice.
This is the spell of torturing ice.

I claw and I scratch. I screech and I wail.
This is the spell of the howling gale.

I clash and I crash. I rip asunder.
This is the spell of booming thunder.

I whisper. I stroke. I tickle the trees.
This is the spell of the evening breeze.

I slither. I slide. I drift and I dream.
This is the spell of the murmuring stream.

Spring Snow

Snowflakes
Slip from the sky
Like soft white butterflies,
Brush the trees with their flimsy wings,
Vanish.

Days

I have this great feeling inside me,
Bubbling and fizzing away,
That today will be bright
And full of sunlight,
A happy and glorious day.

I have this sad feeling inside me,
Weighing me down like a stone,
That today will be grey
And gloomy all day,
A dingy and miserable day.

I have this calm feeling inside me,
Soothing me like a soft song,
That today will be warm
Without any storm,
A quiet, quite ordinary day.

Mandy Coe

Mandy Coe is a poet and illustrator who lives in Liverpool, not far from the river Mersey. She's written seven poetry books, and you can hear and read some of them online at Talking Poetry, BBC School Radio and at the Children's Poetry Archive. Her latest collection is *Belonging Street*. She writes for adults and children, but knows that children are far better at reading poetry, as they are daring, curious and can think in pictures.

Amelia Earhart

'. . . fears are paper tigers.'

A ribbon in her hair and mud on her dress
Amelia climbs too high
then, like any child in a tree,
blinks at the dizzying ground and sky.

Amelia spreads the map on her knees
to light the Atlantic with her torch.
She taps the fuel gauge, adjusts her course.
The stars seemed near enough to touch.

Amelia's red Vega roars around
a world of cloud and sun and time,
and whenever a child overcomes
her fears, Amelia still climbs.

Sensing Mother

Dad keeps Mum's favourite dress
deep in the bottom of the ottoman.
Sometimes, when he is at work
I stand listening to the tick of the clock
then go upstairs.

And propping up the squeaky wooden lid,
I dig through layers
of rough, winter blankets
feeling for that touch of silk.
The blue whisper of it, cool
against my cheek.

Other times, the school-test times,
and Dad-gets-home-too-late
to-say-goodnight times
– I wrap the arms of the dress around me,
breathing in a smell, faint as dried flowers.

I remember how she twirled around
– like a swirl of sky.
When I am old enough I will wear it.
Pulling up the white zip,
I'll laugh and spin,
calling out to *my* daughter:
How do I look?

Me & You

The long-legged girl who takes goal-kicks
is me.
I loop my 'j's and 'g's,
twiddle my hair
and wobble a loose tooth
through History yesterday afternoon.

The small shy boy who draws dragons
is you.
You understand mathematics,
make delicious cheese scones
and when my tooth finally falls out
and I cry in surprise,
you hand me a crumpled tissue.

I will be an Olympic athlete;
win two silver medals.
You will be a vet
in whose gentle hands
cats purr and budgies speak.

We don't know this yet
but we will be each other's first date.
One kiss. Nothing more . . . but
for the rest of our lives we will never forget.

In the meantime,
my tongue explores a toothless gap
and you lean over your desk and concentrate
on drawing the feathery, feathery
lines of a dragon's wing.

Night Night

Up those dancers dearest,
climb the wooden hill,
dreams await down Sheet Lane,
the sun is setting still.

Hike the zigzag path,
the moon is rising higher,
take those gallopers two at a time
up to Bedfordshire.

Jump the Sleepytown Express
up those apples and pears,
snug as a bug in a rug you'll be
when you get to Blanket Fair.

The Superpower Song

The frosted words to *Auld Lang Syne*
bring sparkle
to a winter midnight

and singing *Happy Birthday*
makes eyes twinkle
and candlelight dance,

but this song explodes
from erupting volcanos.
This song melted the earth's heart.

Sing this song to locked doors and they swing open.
Its tune is as sweet as treacle
and salty as a bag of crisps.

Its words can be sung
in every tongue. It finds
lost ships and steers them home.

This song has rhythm,
this song has rhyme, clocks tick
faster when this song is sung.

Is it a lullaby? Is it an anthem?
Should this song be taught or banned?
Would you lock up birds

who accidentally whistle its tune?
Wait! Who's that singing . . . ?
Is it you? Is it you?

Thank You

Danke, merci, gracias
for the heat of the sun,
the kindness of teaching,
the smell of fresh bread.

Diolch, nkosi, shur-nur-ah-gah-lem
for the sound of sand,
children singing,
the book and the pen.

Dhannyabad, blagodaria, hvala
for the blue of small flowers,
the bobbing seal's head,
the taste of clean water.

Shukran, rahmat, shukriya
for the stripe of the zebra,
the song of the chaffinch,
the gentleness of snails.

Mh goi, abarka, xièxiè
for the length of time,
the loveliness of eyelashes,
the arc of the ball.

Dziekuje, abrigado, shakkran
for the excitement of falling,
the stillness of night,
for my heart beating, thank you.

The Strawberry-Yogurt Smell of Words

Once we made a telephone
– string, stretched between two yogurt pots.
'Hello? Hello?'
Communication!
You spoke. I heard.

It's a solitary game now,
the thumb-dance of text, beep of fax,
but I still recall the buzz of string,
the strawberry-yogurt
smell of words.

Ruth Awolola

Ruth Awolola is a British Born Nigerian Jamaican author, poet, workshop facilitator and youth worker currently based in Manchester.

She has been writing and performing poetry since 2015 when she was among the winners of the National Youth Slam, Slambassadors UK. She has since performed at the Hay Literature Festival, BBC Edinburgh Fringe Slam and the Brainchild Festival, become a Say Owt Slam Champion, an Obsidian Foundation Alumna and a Roundhouse Slam Finalist as well as securing feature sets at a number of poetry nights across the country.

Ruth writes for a variety of different audiences including poetry for children and young people. In 2018 she was one of five contributors to Rising Stars: New Young Voices in Poetry which went on to be highly commended in the 2018 CLiPPA where she performed in front of hundreds of primary school students at the National Theatre.

Pockets

Her pockets are never empty.
She says pockets are for running.
So she keeps them full,
Stuffs universes into them,
And says it is just the essentials.

She says: if we get stranded,
If aliens take us,
If there's an apocalypse,
There will be no time for bags.

She treats pockets
Like built in spaces for hope.
Lets the weight of it
Pull down her baggy trousers.

Readies herself for any eventuality,
Revels in her own lack of normality.

A Love Letter to the Stars

I have always wanted to be nocturnal,
To live by the light of the moon.
There's something about the stars – they're eternal.
I pray the sun sets soon.

Dreams and wishes and hope and light,
Placed perfectly in the sky.
I'll never understand the power of the night ,
How it fills me with love or why?

There are things I hate about space.
It's far too big and unknown.
But it is my safe place,
I long to call it home.

I'm in love with the stars,
how they are mine and ours.

Small Things

Something worth losing
The feeling of winning
Words that capture feelings
Successful all-in-one orange skin peelings
Laughing until you're wheezing
Hot drinks when it's freezing
Uninterrupted sleeping
And sibling peacekeeping
Trying and striving to make every day better
All of the things that we can do together
The layers of an inside joke

And all the other small things
That give me hope.

On Forgetting that I Am A Tree

A poem in which I am growing.

A poem in which I am a tree,
And I am both appreciated and undervalued.

A poem in which I fear I did not dig into the past,
Did not think about my roots,
Forgot what it meant to be planted.

A poem in which I realise they may try to cut me down.
That I must change with the seasons,
That I do it so well
It looks as if they are changing with me.

A poem in which I remember I have existed for centuries,
That centuries are far too small a unit of measurement.
That time found itself in the forests, woods and jungles.
Remember I have witnessed creation,
That I am key to it.

A poem in which some will carve their names into my skin
In hopes the universe will know them.
Where I am so tall I kiss the sun.
Trees cannot hide,
They belong to the day and to the night,
To the past and the future.

A poem in which I stop
    looking for it,
Because I am home.
I am habitat.
My branches are host and
    shelter.
I am life-giver and
    fruit-bearer.
Self-sufficient protection.

A poem in which I
    remember I am a tree.

Where I'm From

After George Ella Lyon

I am from makeshift jumper goal posts,
Hand me downs and uniforms two sizes too big;
I am from the stinging of the scraped knee,
Scorned by uneven pavement,
The ringing of the start of day in the near distance;
I am from the aftermath of altercation,
The defiant sway of the head,
(Dancing in rhythmic unison)
At the end of a wagging finger.

I am from the games played on long car journeys,
The things the corner of the eye sees out of the window,
From the impatient moon in the afternoon sky
The comets confused for shooting stars
From hoping and believing
Chance meetings and the miracles that follow

I am from the sweetness of occasion,
Candy clouded memories and summer-long friendships;
I am from the zest it takes to laugh,
And the humility required to do the opposite.

There was a story my mother would share,
That she first heard miles away,
Where the animals talked,
And the sun shone most of the day;
I am from fable, from legend, prayer and myth,
From the true and last goodbye, from the very first kiss.

Write Me A Poem

Mrs Taylor says, 'Pick up a pen,
and write me a poem.'
I had so many things to say,
but I didn't even know them.

Poems seem so structured,
like they take time to organise.
What makes me a poet?
Where can I get authorised?

She says, 'You need to pick up a pen,
And just get started.
It doesn't matter if it's messy,
We just care where your heart is.

You can write about anything and anywhere.
Write about Sweden, Senegal, about Space,
Write at school, in your bed, and on the train.
Write about love,
Write about hope,
Write about pain,
Write about the sun and the wind and the rain
Write about anything,
Just tell me what's in your brain.'

Ta, Love

There's something about the rich tea biscuits
    dipped in a sugary brew,
From the inside, it warms you up.
Something of the feeling ever so welcome
When Dylan's mom says,
'Ta, love.'

John Agard

John Agard was born on 21 June 1949 in Guyana. He moved to England in 1977 with his partner, the poet Grace Nichols. He worked for the Commonwealth Institute, travelling to schools throughout the UK to promote a better understanding of Caribbean culture.

In 1993 he was appointed Writer in Residence at the South Bank Centre, London, and became Poet in Residence at the BBC, an appointment created as part of a scheme run by the Poetry Society. He won the Paul Hamlyn Award for Poetry in 1997.

John has written many children's poems and books. With his partner, Grace Nichols, he co-edited the anthology *Under the Moon and Over the Sea*, which received the first CLPE Children's Poetry Award. He was given the Queen's Gold Medal for Poetry in 2012 and BookTrust's Lifetime Achievement Award in 2021.

First Morning

I was there on that first morning of creation
when heaven and earth occupied one space
and no one had heard of the human race.

I was there on that first morning of creation
when a river rushed from the belly of an egg
and a mountain rose from a golden yolk.

I was there on that first morning of creation
when the waters parted like magic cloth
and the birds shook feathers at the first joke.

Poetry Jump-up

Tell me if Ah seeing right
Take a look down de street

Words dancin
words dancin
till dey sweat
words like fishes
jumpin out a net
words wild and free
joinin de poetry revelry
words back to back
words belly to belly

Come on everybody
come and join de poetry band
dis is poetry carnival
dis is poetry bacchanal
when inspiration call
take yu pen in yu hand
if yu don't have a pen
take yu pencil in yu hand
if yu don't have a pencil
what the hell
so long as de feeling start to swell
just shout de poem out

Words jumpin off de page
tell me if Ah seein right

words like birds
jumpin out a cage
take a look down de street

words shakin dey waist
words shaking dey bum
words wit black skin
words wit white skin
words wit brown skin
words wit no skin at all
words huggin up words
an sayin I want to be a poem today
rhyme or no rhyme
I is a poem today
I mean to have a good time

Words feeling hot hot hot
big words feelin hot hot hot
lil words feelin hot hot hot
even sad words cant help
tappin dey toe
to de riddum of de poetry band

Dis is poetry carnival
dis is poetry bacchanal
so come on everybody
join de celebration
all yu need is plenty perspiration
an a little inspiration
plenty perspiration
an a little inspiration

Checking Out Me History

Dem tell me
Dem tell me
Wha dem want to tell me

Bandage up me eye with me own history
Blind me to me own identity

Dem tell me bout 1066 and all dat
Dem tell me bout Dick Whittington and he cat
But Toussaint L'Ouverture
no dem never tell me bout dat

Toussaint[1]
a slave
with vision
lick back
Napoleon
battalion
and first Black

Republic born
Toussaint de thorn
to de French
Toussaint de beacon
of de Haitian Revolution

Dem tell me bout de man who discover de balloon
and de cow who jump over de moon
Dem tell me bout de dish run away with de spoon
but dem never tell me bout Nanny de maroon[2]

Nanny
see-far woman
of mountain dream
fire-woman struggle
hopeful stream
to freedom river

Dem tell me bout Lord Nelson and Waterloo
but dem never tell me bout Shaka de great Zulu
Dem tell me bout Columbus and 1492
but what happen to de Caribs[3] and de Arawaks too

Dem tell me bout Florence Nightingale and she lamp
and how Robin Hood used to camp
Dem tell me bout old King Cole was a merry ole soul
but dem never tell me bout Mary Seacole[4]

From Jamaica
she travel far
to the Crimean War
she volunteer to go
and even when de British said no
she still brave the Russian snow
a healing star

among the wounded
a yellow sunrise
to the dying

Dem tell me
Dem tell me wha dem want to tell me
But now I checking out me own history
I carving out me identity.

Notes:

1. Toussaint L'Ouverture. Rarely mentioned in school history books. A slave who led an army that defeated forces sent by Napoleon.
2. Nanny. A national heroine of Jamaica. She led runaway slaves to establish a free colony in the hills of Jamaica.
3. Caribs. Amerindian tribe from whom the Caribbean got its name.
4. Mary Seacole. The Jamaican nurse who put her skills to use in the Crimean War (1853–6) but who did not receive the acclaim that Florence Nightingale did.

Secret

Tell me your secret.
I promise not to tell.
I'll guard it safely at the bottom of a well.

Tell me your secret.
Tell me, tell me, please.
I won't breathe a word, not even to the bees.

Tell me your secret.
It will be a pebble in my mouth.
Not even the sea can make me spit it out.

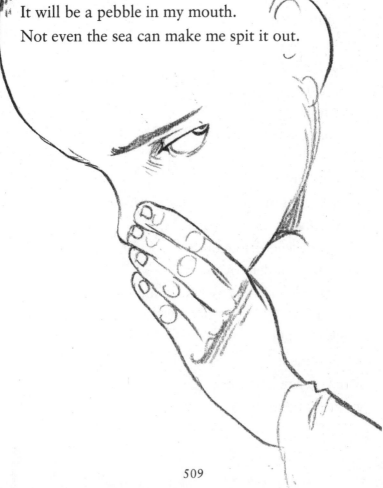

Half-Caste

Excuse me
standing on one leg
I'm half-caste

Explain yuself
wha yu mean
when yu say half-caste
yu mean when Picasso
mix red an green
is a half-caste canvas /
explain yuself
wha yu mean
when yu say half-caste
yu mean when light an shadow
mix in de sky
is a half-caste weather

well in dat case
england weather
nearly always half-caste
in fact some o dem cloud
half-caste till dem overcast
so spiteful dem don't want de sun pass
ah rass /
explain yuself
wha yu mean
when yu say half-caste
yu mean tchaikovsky

sit down at dah piano
an mix a black key
wid a white key
is a half-caste symphony

Explain yuself
wha yu mean
Ah listening to yu wid de keen
half of mih ear
Ah looking at yu wid de keen
half of mih eye
an when I'm introduced to yu
I'm sure you'll understand
why I offer yu half-a-hand

an when I sleep at night
I close half-a-eye
consequently when I dream
I dream half-a-dream
an when moon begin to glow
I half-caste human being
cast half-a-shadow
but yu must come back tomorrow

wid de whole of yu eye
an de whole of yu ear
an de whole of yu mind

an I will tell yu
de other half
of my story

Rainbow

When you see
de rainbow
you know
God know
wha he doing –
One big smile
across the sky –
I tell you
God got style
the man got style

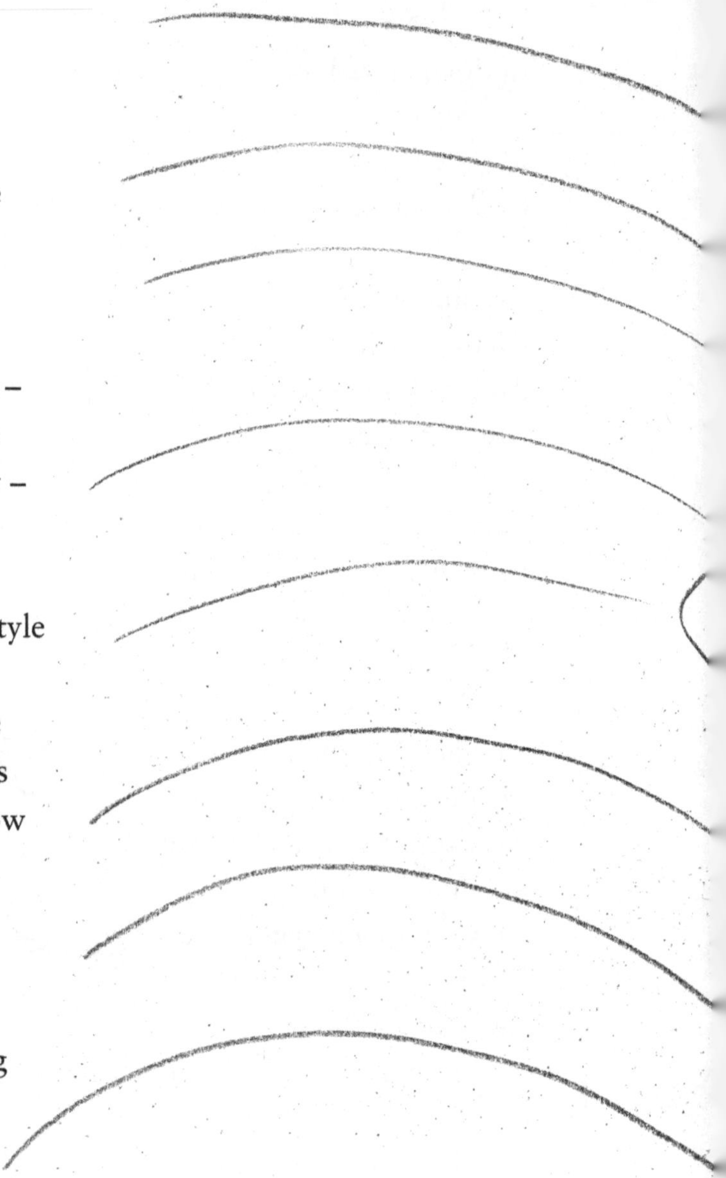

When you see
raincloud pass
and de rainbow
make a show
I tell you
is God doing
limbo
the man doing
limbo

But sometimes
you know
when I see
de rainbow
so full of glow
and curving
like she bearing a child
I does want to know
if God ain't a woman

If that is so
the woman got style
man she got style

The Soldiers Came

The soldiers came
and dropped their bombs.
The soldiers didn't take long
to bring the forest down.

With the forest gone
the birds are gone.
With the birds gone
who will sing their song?

But the soldiers forgot
to take the forest
out of the people's hearts.
The soldiers forgot
to take the birds
out of the people's dreams.
And in the people's dreams
the birds still sing their song.

Now the children
are planting seedlings
to help the forest grow again.
They eat a simple meal of soft rice
wrapped in a banana leaf.
And the land welcomes their smiling
like a shower of rain.

Wes Magee

Wes Magee was born in Scotland and worked as a teacher and head teacher until he became a full-time writer over thirty years ago. He published over 100 books for children, including poetry, picture books and storybooks. He regularly visited schools, libraries and festivals across the UK and abroad, performing his 'poetry show'. His best-known books are *The Very Best of Wes Magee*, published by Macmillan Children's Books, which won the Children's Poetry Bookshelf Award, *The Boneyard Rap* and *The Witch's Brew*. He lived in Yorkshire with his wife, pet dog and many fish and tadpoles!

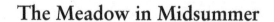

The Meadow in Midsummer

Immobilized by June heat
the chestnut trees are calm cathedrals
    of bough and leaf.
In their deep shade
half-hidden horses
    seek cool relief.

The pond's azure eye
gazes amazed at the gold coin
    dazzling the sky
as, barefoot amidst buttercups,
we cross the meadow,
    slowly pass by.

At the End of a School Day

It is the end of a school day
    and down the long drive
come bag-swinging, shouting children.
    Deafened, the sky winces.
        The sun gapes in surprise.

Suddenly the runners skid to a stop,
    stand still and stare
at a small hedgehog
    curled up on the tarmac
        like an old, frayed cricket ball.

A girl dumps her bag, tiptoes forward
    and gingerly, so gingerly
carries the creature
    to the safety of a shady hedge.
        Then steps back, watching.

Girl, children, sky and sun
    hold their breath.
There is silence,
    a moment to remember
        on this warm afternoon in June.

The Boneyard Rap

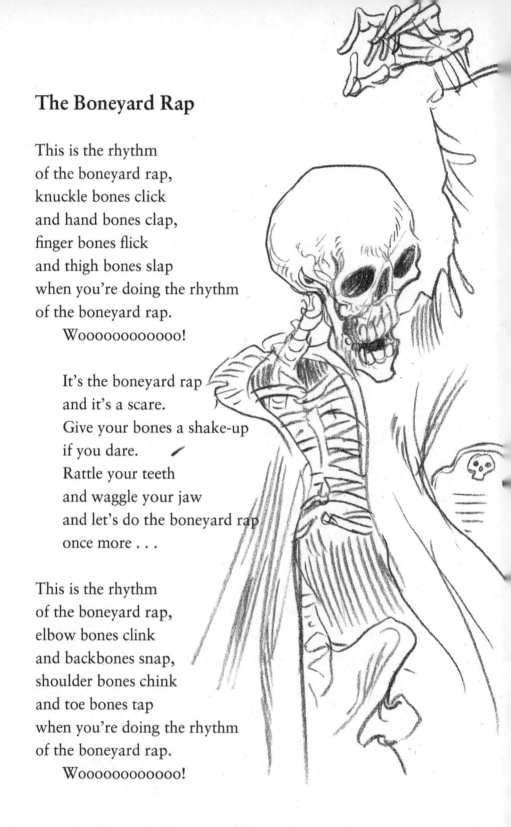

This is the rhythm
of the boneyard rap,
knuckle bones click
and hand bones clap,
finger bones flick
and thigh bones slap
when you're doing the rhythm
of the boneyard rap.
    Wooooooooooooo!

    It's the boneyard rap
    and it's a scare.
    Give your bones a shake-up
    if you dare.
    Rattle your teeth
    and waggle your jaw
    and let's do the boneyard rap
    once more . . .

This is the rhythm
of the boneyard rap,
elbow bones clink
and backbones snap,
shoulder bones chink
and toe bones tap
when you're doing the rhythm
of the boneyard rap.
    Wooooooooooooo!

It's the boneyard rap
and it's a scare.
Give your bones a shake-up
if you dare.
Rattle your teeth
and waggle your jaw
and let's do the boneyard rap
once more . . .

This is the rhythm
of the boneyard rap,
ankle bones sock
and arm bones flap,
pelvic bones knock
and knee bones zap
when you're doing the rhythm
of the boneyard rap.
    Woooooooooooo!

What is . . . the Sun?

The Sun is an orange dinghy
    sailing across a calm sea.

It is a gold coin
    dropped down the drain in Heaven.

The Sun is a yellow beach ball
    kicked high into the summer sky.

It is a thumbprint
    on a sheet of pale blue paper.

The Sun is a milk bottle's gold top
    floating in a puddle.

Footballers in the Park

December. Wet Saturday in the park.
It's late afternoon and it's growing dark

as a bevy of boys play their football game.
Most wear baggy shorts. One goalie's lame.

Posts are old jerseys and hand-me-down coats;
the boys' boots are bulky as rowing boats.

Leather ball's sodden and heavy with mud.
It thumps a boy's face with a squelchy thud

and blood dribbles down from a nose struck numb:
a fat lad stunningly skids on his bum.

One boy shivers in his 'Wednesday' shirt,
the collar's ripped and he's plastered with dirt.

The game rattles on; chill drizzle sets in.
The wind in the trees makes a Cup Final din.

Distantly, lights shine on the wet street
unnoticed by boys whose thundering feet

are playing the game. But the hour grows late.
Here comes the park keeper to padlock the gate.

And the year is 1948.

Instructions for the Last Day in October

Leave the cottage at dusk.
Proceed to the sheep's skull
rammed on the gatepost.
Then plod the sodden field
where mists have gathered
to mutter like shawled hags.
Now enter the indigo wood.
Above, rooks will be cawing in
the coming night.
Note the trees' last leaves
hanging like withered hearts.
At the deep ditch's cauldron
crouch and feel the woodland cringe
in the grip of thistles.
Watch, watch spellbound,
as bubbles rise from the oily ooze
and know then you have arrived
    at
    Hallowe'en.

Pleasant Scents

The kitchen just before lunch on Christmas Day . . .
Salty spray when waves crash on rocks in the bay . . .
In school, when you model with clammy damp clay . . .
>*Pleasant scents*
>*that stay with you*
>>*forever.*

The attic's dry air after days of June heat . . .
A shower of spring rain that refreshes the street . . .
An orange you peel: the tang sharp, yet so sweet . . .
>*Pleasant scents*
>*that stay with you*
>>*forever.*

The Bonfire Night smoke as it drifts in the dark . . .
Air lemony-clean on the Island of Sark . . .
Mint in the back garden . . . and mud in the park . . .
>*Pleasant scents*
>*that stay with you*
>>*forever.*

Michaela Morgan

Michaela is not particularly big but she is amazing – so are you! She has published about 200 books including fiction, non-fiction and picture books. *Never Shake a Rattlesnake* (illustrated by Nick Sharratt) and *Knock! Knock! Open the Door* (illustrated by David Walker) are both published by Macmillan. She was also editor and contributor to the prize-winning *Reaching the Stars: Poems About Extraordinary Women and Girls* and *Wonderland: Alice in Poetry*. She is currently working on producing a book of her collected poems, so you will, one day, be able to find them all in one place.

Star

Twinkle, twinkle, little star
Scientists tell us what you are.
Hydrogen . . . and helium?
Oxygen and nitrogen . . .
Twinkle, twinkle, little star
Is that really what you are?

Twinkle, twinkle, little spark
Bravely twinkling in the dark
We come out to gaze at you,
When we worry what to do.
We find up there a ray of light.
A hope, a comfort in the night
Twinkle, twinkle little star!
Is hope and comfort what you are?

Twinkle, twinkle, I have a clue!
They say we're made of stardust too.
Made to shine, made to gleam
to imagine and to dream
twinkle twinkle little star
– a friend to us is what you are.

Twinkle twinkle little child,
In the garden running wild
Full of laughter, free and light
I hope your future will be bright
Twinkle Twinkle you'll go far
Shine on bravely – you're the star.

My First Day at School

14 November 1960. New Orleans, USA. Ruby Bridges, aged six, is the first Black child to enter an all-white elementary school. She was escorted in by armed guards as protesters shouted abuse at her.

I remember . . .
Momma scrubbed my face, hard.
Plaited my hair, tight.
Perched a hopeful white bow on my head,
Like a butterfly hoping for flight.

She shone my shoes, black, shiny, neat.
Another hopeful bow, on each toe,
To give wings to my feet.

My dress was standing to attention,
   stiff with starch.
My little battledress.
And now, my march.

Two marshals march in front of me.
Two marshals march behind of me.
The people scream and jeer at me.
Their faces are red, not white.

The marshals tower above me, a grey-legged wall.
Broad of back, white of face and tall, tall, tall.
I only see their legs and shoes as black and shiny as mine.
They march along, stern and strong. I try to march in time.

One hisses to another, 'Slow down it ain't a race.
She only takes little bitty girlie steps.'
I quicken my pace.

Head up.
Eyes straight.
I march into school.
To learn like any other kid can.

And maybe to teach a lesson too.

Malala

Malala Yousafzai, born 12 July 1997, is a Pakistani activist known mainly for her defence of human rights and education for girls. On the afternoon of 9 October 2012, Malala boarded her school bus in the Swat district of Pakistan and was approached by a gunman, who asked her name and then fired three shots of a pistol at her head. She survived, recovered, and continues her fight for rights. She is now the youngest ever winner of the Nobel Peace Prize.

A girl with a book.
A girl with a book.
That's what has scared them –
A girl, with a book.

They get on to the bus.
They call out my name.
They aim. And they fire.
A shot to the brain.

Because a girl with a book,
A girl with a voice,
A girl with a brain,
A girl with a choice,
A girl with a plan
To have rights, like a man.
That's what they're scared of,
One girl, with a book.

A girl who has words.
A girl with a pen.
A girl to be heard
With support of her friends
Who want to live free –
That's what they fear,
A girl just like me.

She Finds Fossils

She sells seashells on the seashore –
Ammonite and belemnite
And much much more.
She's not a grand professor
Or a rich and famous man.
She's just a girl who earns her keep
And does the best she can.

She finds fossils on the cliff face.
She digs and dusts, makes her notes,
then presents her case.
There are scrapes, escapes and danger
Land slides, wild seas, wet sands
But with hammer, pick and basket
She does the best she can.

And . . . she discovers dinosaurs!
Plesiosaurus!
Ichthyosaurus too!
And lots and lots of coprolite – or . . . dinosaur poo!
She saw a Pterosaur – so she earned some fame,
Acknowledgement and some applause.
She began to make her name.

She found fame – but she deserved more.
Women like her were not expected to explore.
You can look up Mary Anning. Excavate, unearth her glory!
Dig away, make a display . . .
. . . and tell the world
    HER STORY.

Big Fat Budgie

I'm a
big fat budgie

I don't do a lot.

Might park on my perch.
Might peck at my pot. Might peek
at my mirror. Might ring my bell.
Might peer through the bars
of my fat budgie cell.
Might say 'Who's a pretty boy then';

Might not.
I'm a
big fat
budgie.
I don't
do a
lot.

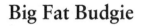

Hello

Hi . . . hello . . . Off we go
G'day and hey
Let's get on with the show

Ekuabo – and salut
Glad to meet ya
Howdy doo?

Assalaam Alaikum
Guten tag
Ciao

Bonjour Hola
Ni hao
and How

Etisen
Bienvenue
How ya doing!
Fine and you?

Namaste Shalom – Yassou
Buenas dias
Big up to you
Hanishiwa and
Yo!

We all just want to say Hello

Love Hearts
Sweets for the Sweet

*Have you ever had those sweets called Love Hearts? They are
pastel, fizzy – and they have messages on them. I used the messages
to make a story and I used the story to make a poem.*

February 14th
playing Cupid
girl on my table acting stupid
passing sweets to me.

They say  I Love You

and You're so Fine,

my friends crease up at Please Be Mine.

She must have packets of them.

All through maths they come

 Great Guy Don't Blush

Then Trust Me – that kind of mush

It's really getting to me.

So at break I go up to her. All right!
She blinks at me. Her smile is growing.

Offers a sweet – 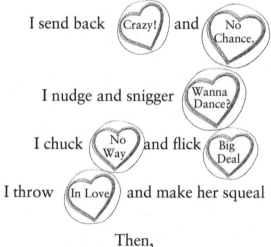 is showing.

I snatch them, push her, run off crowing.

All afternoon I'm thinking how she felt.
I smell the sweet and sickly scent
as pastel messages fizz and melt.

I send back   Crazy!   and   No Chance.

I nudge and snigger   Wanna Dance?

I chuck   No Way   and flick   Big Deal

I throw   In Love   and make her squeal

Then,
when all my friends have gone away
I quietly give her   Don't Cry

and

U. R. O. K.

Index of First Lines

Acknowledgements

The compiler and publisher would like to thank the following for permission to use their copyright material:

Agard, John; 'Poetry Jump Up', 'First', 'Morning The Soldiers Came', copyright © John Agard 1990 reproduced by kind permission of John Agard c/o Caroline Sheldon Literary Agency Ltd. 'Checking Out Me History', 'Secret', 'Half-caste' copyright © John Agard 1996 reproduced by kind permission of John Agard c/o Caroline Sheldon Literary Agency Ltd. 'Rainbow', copyright © John Agard 1983 reproduced by kind permission of John Agard c/o Caroline Sheldon Literary Agency Ltd. **Awolola, Ruth;** 'Pockets', 'A Love Letter to the Stars', 'Small Things', 'On Forgetting that I Am A Tree', 'Where I Am', 'Write Me a Poem', 'Ta, Love', © Ruth Awolola and reprinted by permission of the author. **Benson, Gerard;** 'A Small Star', 'Fishing', from *Evidence of Elephants*, Viking 1995, reprinted by permission of C. Benson, the authors estate, 'Shaking the Branches', 'Wet Playtime' from *Omba Bolomba*, Smith/Doorstop Books 2005 reprinted by permission of C. Benson, the authors estate, 'Spring Assembly', from *The Great Escape*, Macmillan 2000, reprinted by permission of C. Benson, the authors estate, 'Duffy', from *To Catch an Elephant*, Smith/Doorstop Books (2002), reprinted by permission of C. Benson, the authors estate, 'A Tale of Two Citizens', from *Does W Trouble You* (1994), reprinted by permission of C. Benson, the authors estate. **Berry, James;** 'When I Dance', 'One', 'Playing A Dazzler', 'Postcard Poem: Solo', 'A Nest Full of Stars', 'Isn't My Name Magical', 'Okay, Brown Girl, Okay', from *Only One of Me* Macmillan, 2003. **Bevan, Clare;** 'Literacy Hour' from *The Teacher's Revenge*, Ed. Brian Moses, Macmillan, 2003. 'The Music Lesson Rap' from *The Rhyme Riot*, Ed. Gaby Morgan, Macmillan 2002. 'Just Doing My Job' from *We Three Kings*, Ed. Brain Moses, Macmillan 1998. 'The Spider', 'Fairy Names', 'A Flutter of Fairies' from *Fairy Poems*, Macmillan 2004. 'The Mermaid's Garden' from *Mermaid Poems*, Macmillan 2005. **Bilston, Brian;** 'A Brief History of Modern Art in Poetry', 'International Cat Day', 'The Last Bee', 'Penguin Awareness Day' Copyright © Brian Bilston. 'Refugees' from *You Took the Last Bus Home*, Unbound, 2016. Copyright © Brian Bilston. Reprinted by permission. 'The Laws of the Game (Playground Edition)' and '50 Ways to Score a Goal' from *50 Ways to Score a Goal* Macmillan 2021. Copyright © Brian Bilston. Reprinted by permission. **Bloom, Valerie;** 'Pinda Cake', 'Autumn Guilt' and 'Haircut Rap', 'Fruits' and 'Christmas is Here' © Valerie Bloom 2000 from *Let Me Touch the Sky*, Macmillan, reprinted by permission of Eddison Pearson Ltd on behalf of Valerie Bloom. 'How to Ask for a Hamster' and 'Frost' Valerie Bloom 2000 from *The World is Sweet*, Bloomsbury, reprinted by permission of Eddison Pearson Ltd on behalf of Valerie Bloom. **Brownlee, Liz;** 'Puurfect', 'Truth', 'Narwhal', 'Slithering Silver', 'Blackbird', 'Ghoul

Inspectre', 'Christmas Eve' ©Liz Brownlee and reprinted by permission of the author. **Camden, Steven;** 'Prologue', 'First Day', 'Fresh Fish', 'Gazelle', 'Goal', 'Snow', 'Constructs', from *Everything All At Once* Macmillan, 2018, ©Steven Camden and reprinted by permission of the poet. **Carter, James;** 'See It Like A Poet' Copyright © James Carter 2020. 'Love You More', 'Electric Guitars', 'Take A Poem', 'How Easily', 'The Moon Speaks', 'This is Where' from *Weird, Wild & Wonderful: The Poetry World of James Carter* Reprinted by permission of Otter-Barry Books. **Causley, Charles;** 'Timothy Winters', 'I Love My Darling Tractor', 'I am the Song', 'Early in the Morning', 'I Had a Little Cat', 'Good Morning, Mr Croco-doco-dile', 'All Day Saturday' from *Collected Poems for Children*, Macmillan, reproduced by permission of David Higham Associates. **Coe, Mandy;** 'Amelia Earhart' First published in *A Poem for Every Day of the Year*, Macmillan, 'Sensing Mother' first published in Sensational ed Roger McGough, Macmillan. 'Me & You', First published in Read Me At School ed Gaby Morgan, 2009. 'Thank You', 'Night Night' First published in *If You Could See Laughter*, Salt Children's Poetry 2010. 'The Superpower Song' First published in *Poems for Eight Year Olds*, Macmillan 2022. 'The Strawberry-Yogurt Smell of Words' First published *in The Works 5*, Macmillan. **Coelho, Joseph;** 'Make it bigger, Eileen!', 'Miss Flotsam', 'Hamster! Hamster!', 'Siblings', 'Conquer', from *Werewolf Club Rules* published by Frances Lincoln Children's Books, an imprint of The Quarto Group, copyright © 2014. Reproduced by permission of Quarto Publishing Plc. 'Books Have Helped Me', 'If All the World Were Paper' from *Over Heard in a Tower Block* (Otter-Barry Books, 2017). **Conlon, Dom;** 'Quietly Remarkable' first published in *This Rock That Rock* (illus Viviane Schwarz). 'The Way Planets Talk' first published in *Watcher of the Skies* (ed Rachel Piercey). 'Draw Me' first published in *Shaping The World*, ed Liz Brownlee, Macmillan. 'Seeing' first published by the BBC. 'How Stars Die', 'Bentback', 'Swift by Your Side', reprinted by permission of the author. **Cookson, Paul;** 'Let No One Steal Your Dreams', 'Full of Surprises', 'Coolscorin' Matchwinnin' Celebratin' Striker!', 'Crazy at the Zoo', 'Go Explore the Countryside', 'Friends Forever', 'Sea Shoals See Shows on the Sea Bed', ©Paul Cookson, reprinted by permission of the author. **Corbett, Pie;** 'Praise Poem', 'The Playground Monster', 'Secret Poem', 'A Chance in France', 'The Inventor's Wife Speaks', 'Winter Haiku', 'The Dragon Whistler', first published in *Evidence of Dragons*, Macmillan, ©Pie Corbett, reprinted by permission of the author. **Darling Robertson, Shauna;** 'Art Therapy', 'One Whole Minute' and 'Things People Have Told Me in the Past Few Weeks' from *You Are Not Alone*, Troika, 2022; 'A Matter Of [ ]', 'Earthtalk', 'The Followers' and 'The Poetry Guerilla' from *Saturdays at the Imaginarium*, Troika, 2020. All poems © Shauna Darling Robertson and reproduced by kind permission of Troika. **Dean, Jan;** 'It's Not What I'm Used To' from, *A Mean Fish Smile,* Macmillan 2000. 'Angels', *Nearly Thirteen,* Blackie 1994. 'Midnight' and 'Tent', from *Wallpapering the Cat,* Macmillan 2003. 'Colouring In', from *Mice on Ice,* Macmillan 2004. 'Rosa Parks' and 'June 1963' from *Reaching the Stars,* Macmillan 2017. **Dixon, Peter;** 'Magic Cat', 'Lone Mission', 'Grown-ups', 'Poetry Day', 'Missing Important Things', 'Why?' and 'The Penguin in the Fridge', reprint by permission of the author's estate. **Donaldson,**

547

(Two Rivers Press 2008); 'Between the Covers' first published in *Poems for 8 Year Olds* (Macmillan 2022); 'Troll Song' from *Things You Find In A Poet's Beard* (Burning Eye Books 2015); and 'Parasol (Just a Light Shower)' is published here for the first time. Copyright © A.F. Harrold. Reproduced by kind permission of the poet. **Joseph, Jenny;** 'The Magic of the Brain', 'Having Visitors', 'The Things I See', 'The Life of Feet', 'Warning', 'Getting Back Home', 'Another Story of Red Riding Hood', Reproduced by permission of Johnson & Alcock Ltd. **Kay, Jackie;** 'Grandpa's Soup' from *The Frog Who Dreamed She Was An Opera Singer*, Bloomsbury;' Vault' from *Bantam*, Picador, 'Promise', 'Sassenachs', 'Brendon Gallacher', The Moon at Knowle Hill', 'Summer Romance', from *Darling: New & Selected Poems, Bloodaxe.* **McMillan, Ian** 'Counting the Stars', 'Ready Salted', 'Ten Things Found in a Shipwrecked Sailor's Pocket', 'Routes', 'Robinson Crusoe's Wise Sayings', 'The Music I Like', 'Ten One Line Poems About Sport' copyright © Ian McMillan, reprinted by permission of the author. **Magee, Wes;** 'The Meadow in Midsummer', 'At the End of a School Day', 'Footballers in the Park', 'Instructions for the Last Day in October' from *A Poem for Every Day of the Year* Macmillan 1998. 'Boneyard Rap' from *The Boneyard Rap and Other Poems* Hodder Wayland. 'Pleasant Scents' from *A First Poetry Book* ed Gaby Morgan and Pie Corbett, Macmillan Children's Books. **McGough, Roger;** 'I'm Not as Nice as I Look', 'First Day at School', 'The Sound Collector', 'The Fight of the Year', 'Give and Take', 'What I Love About School', 'Joy at the Sound', copyright Roger McGough. Printed by permission of United Agents (www.unitedagents.co.uk) on behalf of Roger McGough. **Morgan, Michaela;** 'Star', 'My First Day At School', 'Malala', 'She Finds Fossils', 'Big Fat Budgie', 'Love Hearts', Copyright Michaela Morgan, previously published by Macmillan, 'Hello', reprinted by permission of the author. **Moses, Brian;** 'Aliens Stole My Underpants', 'Make Friends with a Tree', 'Lost Magic', 'A Feather from an Angel', 'Walking with my Iguana', 'Days', 'Things You Can Say to Places in the UK' from *Lost Magic: The Very Best of Brian Moses* published by Macmillan Children's Books in 2016. **Mucha, Laura;** 'Collage', 'Night Flight', 'Listening To', 'Fleming's Petri Dish', 'Compliments of Shakespeare', 'You're Never Too', 'I'm An Orchestra', reproduced by permission of David Higham Associates. **Nichols, Grace;** 'Morning', 'Give Yourself a Hug', 'Teenage Earthbirds' from *Give Yourself A Hug* Copyright © Grace Nichols 1994, 'For Forest', Granny Granny Please Comb My Hair', from *Come On Into My Tropical Garden* Copyright © Grace Nichols 1988, 'Mama-Wata' from *No Hickory No Dickory No Dock* Copyright © Grace Nichols 1991, 'Tabby' from *Orchard Books Anthology* Copyright © Grace Nichols, Reproduced with permissions from Curtis Brown Group Ltd on behalf of Grace Nichols. **Orme, David;** 'Guess the Title!', 'July 20th 1969 - What they didn't find on the Moon', 'Football in the Rain' 'Tyrannosaurus Chicken', 'Home Time at Half Past Three', 'Beside the Seaside', 'Don't Feed the Yeti', Reprinted by permission of the author. **Owen, Gareth;** 'Den to let' and 'Saturdays' first published in *Salford Road*, Kestrel. 'Miss Creedle teaches Creative Writing', 'The Commentator' first published in *Song of the City*, Harper Collins. 'Gathering in the Days' first published in *Gathering in the Days*, Collins Big Cat. 'Saturday night at the Bethlehem Arms' and 'Bird' first published in *Icarus*

What are We Fighting For

The Big Amazing Poetry Book

Only One of Me

Crazy Mayonnaisy Mum

She Will Soar

We Wish You A Merry Christmas

A First Poetry Book

Sensational!

Reaching the Stars

Poems to Save the World With